SAVY
WISDOM

From Beyond

By
New York Times Best-Selling Author
Peggy McColl

Hasmark
PUBLISHING
INTERNATIONAL

ISBN-13: 978-1-77482-196-1

ISBN-10: 1774821966

Published by:

Hasmark Publishing International

Important Disclaimers

Cover design by Killer Covers
Book layout by Trace Haskins
Editing by Kathryn Young
First Edition, 2023

Praise for Savy Wisdom From Beyond

"Savy Wisdom From Beyond is an amazing 5-star read! It opens your mind to the magical world of possibilities and how to see things differently about life and death. This book is the third of a series of three and while I truly enjoyed the first two I have to say this one is my favorite! It is beautifully written and the fact that the story is inspired by real events makes it even more interesting. I also loved the unexpected plot twists I couldn't put it down!"

~ L.L. Tremblay, Author of Seven Roses
   and Light Over Dark

"Once I started reading Savy Wisdom From Beyond I couldn't put it down! The intrigue of what would happen next kept my attention throughout. This book is jam-packed with sage advice and real life lessons that everyone can relate to and benefit from. Peggy McColl has hit a Grand Slam with Savy Wisdom from Beyond."

~ Linda Proctor

"Have you ever lost someone you loved? Savy Wisdom From Beyond may be a fiction book, but the lessons inside are very real: about powerfully dealing with grief, loss, and challenging situations. It also offers a new perspective on life and death; one that can completely change the way you live, and the way you experience your loved ones who have passed on. It's an easy read that inspires you to understand and embody some very deep principles - I highly recommend you dive right in."

~ Trace Haskins, Author, Prosperous On Purpose

"Savy Wisdom From Beyond is a page-turner of a story that delivers life-transforming insights and lessons that are both practical and mystical. While the main theme is about dying and grief, surprisingly this is an uplifting book about death. Given that we are all going to die, along with everyone we have ever loved, this is a must-read for all."

~ Arielle Ford, Author, The Soulmate Secret:
    Manifest The Love Of Your Life With
    The Law of Attraction

"Outstanding and brilliantly written. This book is essential reading for anyone looking to understand how the mind can be programmed to its fullest potential. This magical story will also guide you to have a powerful knowledge of the life and death that intertwines all around us. An exciting, captivating and must read book with tonnes of valuable lessons that will positively impact your life and the lives of millions of people forever."

~ Roddy Telfer, Business, Mindset and Marketing Coach

"Savy Wisdom From Beyond brings such new and much needed understanding and awareness about grief, death and dying. The enlightenment and energy leaps off the pages and provides such hope for what is possible, as humans as we live, and as we transition from this world. I highly recommend this book to all to read."

~ Marilyn Adams

"Savy Wisdom From Beyond is not only a superb read but a lighthouse for your journey… a journey on which you can experience the best but also the worst. It truly depends on your perception and committed irrevocable decisions you take… while listening to (or ignoring) your intuition and divine guidance. I was fully absorbed in the present moment and I believe Peggy wrote the book at perfect time for billions of souls that may feel lost. If you are dealing with the loss of someone, this book gives you peace. I love how it opened up my consciousness even more and I know I am on the right emotional path and that I have always understood and lived in alignment with the Higher Power. Read this book as the awareness shifts in ways meant for you!"

~ Vladimira Kuna, Int'l Best-Selling Author,
The Bible of the Masterminds

"I love reading books that inspire and bring hope. Occasionally I find one I consider a jewel, a gift. Savy Wisdom From Beyond is definitely one of those books; it strummed the strings of my soul."

~ Robert Pascuzzi, Film Producer and Author, The Ravine

"Peggy, you've done it again! You have created a beautiful story of inspiration, love and hope. From the beginning to end, you captivate the reader. I read it in one sitting as I couldn't wait to see what happened next. Thank you for continuing this series!"

~ Jayne Lowell

"Supernatural. In the third installment of the Savy Wisdom series, McColl takes the reader on a thoughtful and uplifting examination of mortality and death. Every chapter oozes wisdom applicable to every aspect of our mortal lives. By viewing death as a gift, the living can reframe a loved one's passing (as well as their own) simply as a transition to a new phase on their eternal journey. Embrace life in the face of death and be at peace."

~ M. Shawn Petersen, Author, Stella And The Timekeepers

"WOW! Savy Wisdom From Beyond is, by far, my favourite in the series. Well done! I connected with the story and felt it deeply. I believe this book will help many people deal with grief in a positive way."

~ Judy O'Beirn, President of Hasmark Publishing

"Savy Wisdom From Beyond is a genuinely remarkable and captivating book that I found myself unable to put down. It's beautifully written, and the lovely detail and inspiring message keeps you wanting more. It gives new meaning to the word grief. I wish more people could find comfort like I found in this book when losing someone you love. It would help so many people learn to deal with grief differently. This book will bring you comfort and wisdom and potentially change your perspective on life after death. Its message is truly unique and one you haven't heard before."

~ Kayla Léon, Author of the Children's Book,
    "What A Mess Kid"

"Well she's done it again! Peggy McColl has produced another triumph in Savy Wisdom 3 - the perfect evolution of the Savy storyline with a powerful message about what happens after death. A must read for anyone struggling with the loss of a loved one."

~ Tommy Collier, Entrepreneur

"Peggy is a fabulous storyteller and journey master! I was captivated by the first book, Savy Wisdom which is a crossroad that many of us meet in life at some point, a crisis of belief about ourselves and who we truly are. Then, when Savy Wisdom 2 came out it was a reminder of the challenges that we must face and overcome with grace though love and a strength that we can connect to that is within each of us. And now, to meet Savy Wisdom From Beyond, is a testament to a part of life that many of us are fearful of, death and grief. All of these challenges in life can interrupt our attempts at happiness and quickly replace the joy and prosperity we seek in our lives. I love the way Peggy meets these challenges and turns them into opportunities through Sophie. I feel like a part of my own life is being played out to witness and now find other ways to evaluate my life. I'm so grateful for Peggy's genius and generosity to share her life experiences through the story of Sophie and be the wisdom and guide for us during the journey. Beautifully written with powerful messages to support understanding and to choose a life of freedom and joy with a fantastic, talented mentorship of Peggy and her Savy!"

~ Angie Tumlinson, Natural Laws Expert

"I'm really not a big reader. I don't read a lot of books, especially on this topic, but I really loved Savy Wisdom From Beyond. I feel it completes the trilogy perfectly. The ending of this book was amazing and it moved me. I feel anyone who reads this book will look at the grieving process in a different way."

~ Denis Beliveau, Husband of the Author

Table of Contents

Chapter 1

"Sophie! Sophie! Wake up! The baby."

The blaring sound of a man's voice woke me out of my deep sleep. Typically, I was a very light sleeper, but out of sheer exhaustion, I had fallen into a deep slumber.

Sure enough, my baby, Stephen Alexander, affectionally called Little Savy, was crying and very likely hungry and ready for his next feeding.

After picking up my sweet baby boy from his bassinette, I changed his diaper and sat in the rocking chair situated in the corner of the bedroom.

Several months had passed since we were blessed with our ray of sunshine. Little Savy was an adorable, healthy, and happy baby. He was easy to care for. The only challenge I was finding was that he ate often. It seemed every two hours he wanted to be fed, and this occurred around the clock. He was a breast-fed baby, and even though my husband Benny was willing and eager to bottle-feed him, I hadn't yet started pumping. Selfishly, I was enjoying every moment of this amazing mother-baby connection.

Little Savy was gaining weight and getting bigger. We started to notice wonderful changes. He began to lift his head, smile, and make adorable little baby noises.

While nursing Little Savy, I stared at his perfect face. I would get lost in thought of this little miracle. After having an ovary removed, a miscarriage, and several attempts, I wasn't sure I would be able to have a baby, but sure enough, we were truly blessed.

Suddenly it dawned on me that the man's voice that woke me up was very familiar to me. *Wait a minute!* I thought. That booming man's voice was Savy's voice. *How could that be? Was I dreaming? Did I imagine it was him?*

I concluded that it must have been wishful dreaming.

My mentor and dear friend Savy passed away on the day of our son's birth. It was the greatest day of my life, and yet, one of the saddest days too.

On the day of my baby's birth, Savy came to me in a dream at 2:22 a.m. and said, *Don't cry for me. I am in a better place.*

In the dream, Savy and I were sitting on the park bench where we had originally met and had many subsequent meetings that were life-changing for me. Savy said those words, and when we stood up to hug goodbye, he disappeared as I attempted to wrap my arms around him. I woke up from that dream and felt unsettled and confused.

The following morning, after our son was born, we discovered that Savy had passed away at precisely 2:22 a.m.

I knew that Savy was powerful, but how in the world was he able to send me a message in a dream? Yet, that is what I felt at the time and still believe to be true. It was an extraordinary goodbye.

I really missed Savy. I missed our conversations. I missed his guidance. I missed his presence. It was surreal to me that he was no longer a phone call away.

There were many occurrences where I wished I could ask him a question or get his advice. I wanted to know why he had to die. Why did he have to go so soon? Why did he feel it was his time? Why didn't he use his own power to overcome his health challenge? He guided me to overcome mine when I was going through cancer treatments.

Savy passed away from heart failure. During one of our conversations, he shared with me that he was born with congenital heart disease. He confessed that his childhood was less than ideal. Because of his heart condition, he couldn't participate in sports like the other kids. Other children made fun of him. He often felt like he didn't belong. He told me that he was bullied and struggled most of his young life and had a troubling upbringing.

Savy's father left when he was young, and his mother found it difficult to raise a family on her own. Savy said she was a kind and generous woman who did her best to keep a roof over their heads and food on the table.

By the time Savy was a teenager, he felt he might as well just fade away and die. He believed he had no self-worth.

I certainly knew about that type of emotional pain, as I had suffered from the same condition. We were kindred spirits in that we both knew what it felt like to be at the lowest point in life when you have no will to live. To feel as if you were, quite literally, worthless.

Savy told me that, as a teenager, he planned his suicide. He determined the day, the method, and the location where he would end his life. But, on that fateful day, as Savy stood on the overpass, clutching the railing, ready to jump, a bald, middle-aged man with wire-rimmed glasses unexpectedly approached him and struck up a conversation.

Savy wasn't interested in having a conversation with anyone and, at first, felt annoyed. But this man's demeanor, genuine caring nature, and the personal life-altering story that he began to share that day caused Savy to pause and listen.

The stranger asked him: "What if today was a new beginning for you? It is, you know. This day is new. This moment is new. How would you act and feel if you knew you could do anything you desired? What would you do?"

Savy said he was startled by the question and turned to look at this stranger.

The man continued, "I was where you are twenty-four years ago. I didn't want to live another day. It was too painful. I planned to end my life and drove my car directly into an abutment at a high rate of speed. The accident should have caused my death, but it didn't."

The man's unexpected words caught Savy's attention. He dropped one hand from the overpass railing.

"The emergency crew had to use the jaws of life to get me out of my vehicle. I was airlifted to a hospital, underwent several surgeries, and ended up in a coma, where I remained for months. When I woke up, I couldn't move my legs. I was paralyzed from the waist down. If I thought my life was awful before this, it now felt a lot worse. My desire to end my life intensified. I asked the medical professionals to put me out of my misery. Their job was to repair my physical body, and they were doing everything in their power to help me regain physical strength. However, the emotional pain was deep."

Savy dropped his other hand from the railing and stared at the stranger with growing curiosity.

"The paralysis was temporary, and with physical therapy, they informed me I would be able to walk again. They suggested it would be a long healing road ahead."

"Why are you telling me this?" Savy asked the man.

"I have something I would like to give you, but first, let me tell you the rest of my story. During my physical therapy, I met a little girl who had more determination than anyone I had ever met. She was persistent beyond persistent. She had lost her leg in a horrible snowmobile accident. Her father was driving and went through a wire fence, and he was killed instantly. Not only was this little girl healing from the pain of losing her father, but she lost her leg and was learning how to walk again with the use of a prosthesis. She also had suffered head trauma, and her balance was completely off."

Savy felt a growing empathy for this young girl's double tragedy.

"I watched this girl stand and fall. She would get back up and fall again. She did this time and time again until finally, she could stand for a few seconds. She would celebrate every and any little improvement. Her attitude was unlike anyone I had ever met. She was a bright light. She would encourage me to try harder. How could I give up when this little girl was giving it her all? She inspired me to try harder, so I did."

The stranger calmly asked if they could leave the busy overpass and walk to a nearby park bench. Savy followed the man to the bench to hear the rest of his story.

"Her name was Sarah. We became physio buddies, and we both healed over time. This little girl was incredibly wise for her age. The day she was discharged from the hospital, she gave me this poem she wrote. I carry it with me always to remember what she taught me about never giving up, and I want you to have it. Allow this to be your guiding light. It saved my life. Maybe it will save yours too."

The stranger handed Savy the poem. Savy said he glanced down to read it, and when he looked up, the stranger was gone.

I reached into my bedside table drawer to pull out a well-worn copy of the same poem. Savy had given it to me when I was going through cancer treatment.

"Oh, how I miss you, Savy," I said with a sad smile.

In times of pain and challenge,
When you feel the need,
Go within
To find the seed.

Life is precious;
It's a gift.
You get to choose
How high you lift.

When you lose faith
And life gets you down,
Do your best,
Release the frown.

Decide right now
It's time for you
To turn things around.
You have much more to do.

You have a divine purpose;
Discover it today.
It will inspire you
To live in that way.

Greatness is a part
Of your DNA.

Show the world
A better way.

You were born
A child of God.
Loved completely,
Your life is His nod.

At the dawn of each morning
When you open your eyes,
If you feel lost,
Look to the skies.

The answer will always
Be there for you,
Guiding the way
To all that is true.

Today is a fresh day,
A new start,
To invite the feeling
Of joy in your heart.

Chapter 2

Hannah, my television studio producer, was encouraging me to return to my talk show sooner rather than later. Leon, the temporary host who replaced me while on maternity leave, had accepted a new assignment and was going to be leaving the studio at the end of the month.

As much as I loved being a host of my own talk show, I loved being a mom more. The months were flying by quickly, and I wanted to cherish every moment with my baby and complete the full year of maternity leave. After the year was done, I wasn't sure if I was going to be returning to work full time, even though my mom offered to care for our baby while I was at work.

Financially we were fine, as I was still collecting royalty payments from my first book. We also had Benny's income, which was a healthy one, which meant all expenses were easily covered.

My book, *Destiny Treasure*, had been translated into a dozen languages, and royalties were also coming in from foreign rights sales. The publisher asked me to write a second book, but I wasn't feeling inspired to write just yet. I felt oddly indifferent as far as what I was going to do next, but I felt confident the perfect solution would reveal itself in due time.

It was now six months since Savy's passing. The pain of not being able to call him or see him didn't seem to diminish in any way. In fact, I missed him more and more every day that went by.

I yearned to have a conversation with him and to seek his guidance. His passing made me realize how much I truly counted on him. He was my rock. He believed in me. He would put me on the right path if I went off track. He invited me to view things from a different perspective. He showed me how to find the gift or blessing in every situation. I knew he was unique, but there truly wasn't anyone else like him. I was quite certain his wife Carol and his family were missing him deeply.

At times I found myself feeling angry that he died. I wasn't angry at him, just angry at the reality that I would never see him or hear from him again. I would often say out loud, "Why did you have to die, Savy?"

When Savy was alive, he wrote letters to me often. In his final letter, he wrote:

My Dear Sophie,

If you are reading this, then you now know that I am on to the next phase of my eternal journey. Please do not feel sad or shed tears. I am at peace. I will be with you in spirit always, in all ways. Think of me, and I will be with you.

I tried that. I simply thought of him and waited. Nothing. I heard nothing. Felt nothing. I started to wonder whether it was possible to communicate with the spirit of someone who had passed. I wasn't really a believer in this idea, but at this point, I was open to anything.

I started noticing unusual things happening around me, though. For example, one day, I was doing laundry, and while folding a load of clothes, I was surprised to discover the handkerchief Savy gave me when I first met him many years ago. I thought that handkerchief was lost. I searched for it several times and couldn't find it. I assumed it was lost forever, and it saddened me as it was a special gift.

I instantly went back in time to the origin story of the handkerchief. When I was seventeen, my high school sweetheart Chad ended our relationship. I felt devastated. Chad was my world, and up to that point in my life, he was the only person to tell me he loved me. I was completely committed to our relationship. As the expression goes, I was *all in*. The thought of not being Chad's girlfriend was inconceivable. And as ridiculous as it seems now, after the breakup, all I wanted to do was die.

The day after the breakup, I was at the lowest point in my life. I walked to the park early in the morning. I sat on the park bench where Chad and I had engraved our initials into the wood, as this was the location of our first kiss. I sat down and began to cry inconsolably. Then out of the corner of my eye, I could see a hand extended with an embroidered handkerchief. It was a stranger. A well-dressed, tall, elderly gentleman. He caught me by surprise as I thought I was alone in the park. His name was Savy. Later I discovered his given name was Stephen Alexander Vaughan, but everyone knew him as Savy.

The handkerchief was embroidered with these words: *If you want your life to change, you must change.*

That was the beginning of my transformation to a life of happiness and success and an extraordinary bond with a wise and wealthy billionaire by the name of Savy.

Other unusual events also occurred. One day when our sweet Little Savy was swinging in his swing, he was staring upward and smiling and making gurgling noises. The only other time I saw him do this was when Benny sang to him and made funny faces. Benny had a unique ability to make Little Savy smile and laugh often. It was purely delightful to watch. I loved the bond father and son shared.

But on this day, Benny was at work, and Little Savy, swinging away in his automatic swing, was looking up and smiling and gurgling. I wondered what he was looking at. The baby was completely captivated, as if someone was talking to him.

Another day, I hopped in my car to go to the grocery store. Normally, my Power Life Script on my phone would automatically begin to play as my phone was connected wirelessly to the audio player in my vehicle. Not that day. Instead, the song "Pretend" by Nat King Cole began to play, and the volume was rather loud. The lyrics were uplifting: "Pretend you're happy when you're blue. It really isn't that hard to do. And you'll find happiness without an end . . ."

"Pretend" was Savy's favorite song! I didn't even have the song on my own playlist, and my car stereo was off. How in the world could this song be playing? Out of alarm, I turned off the audio on my phone. That experience kind of freaked me out.

On another day, I was taking Little Savy to his first swim class for babies. I entered the address for the pool location into my navigation system. My navigation system directed me to the cemetery and not the pool. I checked the address I entered, and sure enough, it was the proper address. That was very strange.

Oddly enough, I had been thinking of visiting Savy's gravesite but had been putting it off. I had some time to spare before the swim lesson, so I got out of my vehicle, removed Little Savy from his car seat, and walked over to Savy's graveside. Fresh daisies were lying against his headstone. I suspected they may have been from Carol as she loved daisies.

The next event was definitely the most unusual. One afternoon, after I put Little Savy down for his afternoon nap, my telephone rang. I didn't recognize the number but answered the phone quickly so the ringing wouldn't wake up the baby.

"Hello," I answered.

"Hi, may I please speak to Sophie?" a stranger asked.

"This is Sophie."

"Sophie, you don't know me, but my name is Louise, and I was instructed to give you a message."

"Okay," I replied hesitantly. "What is the message, please?" I had no idea where this was going, but she got my attention.

"Would you be open to meeting with me so that I can explain?" Louise requested. "It is important that I meet with you in person."

I started feeling a little irritated. I was a busy mom, didn't get enough sleep as it was, and didn't have a lot of available time to meet with strangers. Feeling a bit annoyed, I asked her, "What is this all about? I'm sorry to be rude, but I have a baby, and he keeps me busy, and I don't have a lot of available time. Would you please tell me what the message is over the telephone?"

"No, sorry, I can't. It is important we meet in person. I am happy to come to you. Trust me, I'm not a weirdo, nor am I going to bring you any harm. This is important." She was almost pleading.

I instinctively felt her voice was sincere. Allowing a stranger into my home wasn't something that I would normally do, but my intuition felt good about this woman. Savy taught me to trust my intuition, so I decided to allow it.

"If you are open to coming to my home, I would be happy to meet with you. My baby naps twice a day, typically mid-morning and mid-afternoon. Would tomorrow morning at 10:30 work for you?"

Louise agreed, and I gave her my address.

As soon as I hung up the phone, I called my mom and told her about the call. Mom agreed to come to the house the following morning so I would not be alone with the baby when this lady came to visit. I felt that was a good idea. Besides, having my mom around was always nice as she automatically jumped in to help with things around the house, including entertaining the baby while I washed up or did a load of laundry.

Louise arrived at my home on time. She was a middle-aged woman, probably in her fifties, with long blonde hair and green eyes. She was extremely petite. She had a warm smile, and I immediately felt as if I had known her or seen her before.

"Louise, have we met before? You look very familiar."

"Yes, we met briefly once before. I was at the book launch party for your book *Destiny Treasure*. Savy invited me. Savy told me all about you. He loved you very much. You were very special to him. Savy and I were friends for many years. In fact, I was his spiritual advisor."

Spiritual advisor? Savy had a spiritual advisor? He did tell me that he had several advisors and guides over the years, but he never mentioned a spiritual advisor.

Suddenly, I felt this rush of excitement. "Louise, is your message from Savy?"

"Yes, it is," she said with a smile. "Is there somewhere we can sit down and talk?"

I led Louise to my kitchen table. My mom was in the nursery playing with Little Savy. He was fed and diaper-changed, and she was going to rock him to sleep and sing him a lullaby. Quality grandma, grandson time.

Louise began as soon as we sat in the chairs.

"Savy came to me with a clear message to deliver to you. He said he has been attempting to reach out."

I interrupted her. "Reach out? What do you mean?"

"He said he has been trying to get messages to you. He placed a handkerchief in your laundry basket. He played a song on the stereo in your vehicle and directed you to go to the cemetery. He said he reveals himself to you in your dreams and speaks to you, but you seem to ignore all these signs."

I was sitting there astonished. First, how would Louise even know about these things? Savy must be communicating with her. It was important that I suspend any disbelief and remain open. After all, I had been longing to communicate with him. I had so many unanswered questions.

"Savy wants you to finish something that he started," Louise told me.

"Finish something? Finish what? What does he want me to finish?"

"That part I do not know. You are instructed to go to his favorite place, and you will be guided further. This is an important project. Savy said it may be the most important project of your life. He said he only trusts you to do this. He believes in you and trusts you. He said that he will send you subsequent messages and for you to remain open to receive them."

And, with that, Louise raised her hands, palms facing me as if to say, "That's it! That's all!"

Chapter 3

Benny returned from work, and we sat on the floor in the living room and played with Little Savy.

"How was your day, honey?" he inquired.

Benny didn't ask me about our day for the sake of conversation. He was genuinely interested and wanted to know every detail, including any new advancements with our baby. I loved the attention he gave to his family. I knew that we were his number one priority.

Oftentimes I would take snapshots or short videos of the baby and send them to him at work. He told me that the photos and videos were the highlights of his day.

I told Benny about the visit with Louise and asked what he thought. He was a little surprised at first but then intrigued. Benny knew Savy very well as they had worked together for many years. It was Savy who introduced me to Benny. In fact, he set us up years before on a blind date. Savy had a highly developed instinct and intuitively felt that Benny and I would be a great match. He was right about that.

I asked Benny if he was aware of any special projects that Savy had been working on.

"Sorry, no idea. Savy wasn't in the office very often. In fact, during the last three years of his life, I didn't see him at the office at all."

"Did he ever mention a favorite place he enjoyed?" I asked.

"Let me think. He did love to hike and would often hike up the mountain, go to the lookout bluff and enjoy the view. Maybe that's his favorite place."

Benny was deep in thought. "Perhaps his favorite place is the park bench where the two of you met?" He started to say it as a statement, but since he wasn't sure, it turned into a question.

"Maybe," I replied doubtfully. That bench was certainly a special place, but would it qualify as his favorite? I had another thought.

"You know, the first time I went to his home, he showed me his library and raved about how much he loved that room. Maybe that was his favorite place."

"I have a suggestion," Benny said, taking my hand with encouragement. "Call Savy's wife Carol and ask her. I am certain she would be able to shed some light."

"Great idea, my love. I will call Carol after dinner."

The idea of calling Carol felt a little uncomfortable. I hesitated to bother her, even though I knew Benny's suggestion was the right direction to take. She was the best person to ask. If anyone knew Savy, it was her. They were together for several decades and had a beautiful and connected marriage.

While Benny gave Little Savy his bath, I called Carol. She answered on the first ring.

"Carol?"

"Yes, this is her," Carol answered.

Carol was a sweet lady, confident yet calm. Her personality was gentle, and her voice soothing to the ears.

"It's Sophie. How are you doing?" I was almost afraid to ask.

It must be a traumatic, life-changing situation for her to no longer have her beloved husband around. I wondered how she was adjusting. I had been so busy with the baby that it had been several weeks since we spoke.

"Oh, Sophie. It is wonderful to hear from you. I am doing okay. How about you? How are you and Benny doing, and how is Little Savy?"

Carol loved the fact that we called our baby after her husband. Ever since his birth, she had showered him with gifts.

"Little Savy is growing like a weed. He's such a good baby, and we are enjoying every minute, even if it means I am sleep deprived," I said with a chuckle.

"Oh, I remember those days," she empathized.

"He's starting to sleep for longer periods. One night he slept for six straight hours. It was heaven. I know it's only a matter of time before he sleeps through the entire night. I'm looking forward to those days, or I should say nights."

We chatted a bit longer about her family and mutual friends before I got around to the main reason I had called.

When I told Carol about the visit with Louise, she didn't seem surprised about the spiritual advisor's psychic connection with Savy. She said Louise was a very gifted spiritualist. I asked if any of Louise's message made sense to her.

"Honestly, Sophie, I have no idea what project Louise is referencing. Savy kept his work stuff to himself. I wasn't always aware of everything he worked on. There were times when he went away to work on projects so he could concentrate."

As far as his favorite places were concerned, Carol said he had several of those. He loved sitting in his garden and watching the birds and the squirrels. He loved to hike and would take off for an afternoon and be gone for hours; however, she was not aware of all the places he hiked.

"He also loved to travel and had a few destinations that he would claim as favorites. He would spend hours in the library in our home and read. That was a heavenly place for him. This is probably not very helpful, is it?"

"It's a start," I assured her. I felt that we would figure it out in time.

"Sophie, you are welcome to come over, and we can have a coffee and discuss this mystery further. Maybe other ideas will come to me. If you are coming for a visit, though, you must bring your beautiful baby."

"Little Savy is a busy little boy. If he came with me, we wouldn't be able to carry on a focused conversation for very long unless he was sleeping. How about if I come over for a visit, and we'll do a visit with Benny and Little Savy another day?"

"Sure, I am happy to do that. My calendar is open. Simply tell me what works for you, and we'll do it."

"There's no time like the present," I stated. "How about tomorrow or the next day?"

"If you can make it tomorrow morning, that would be perfect."

"I will give my mom a call and ask her to watch Little Savy tomorrow, and I'll be over around nine o'clock."

After Carol and I said goodbye, I called my mom, and she responded in her usual fashion. "Absolutely! I'm there!" She was thrilled to babysit her grandson. She was an amazing grandma. Between my siblings and me, she had five grandchildren. She loved her grandchildren to bits. She loved being with them, playing with them, and doing activities with them. It gave me comfort that Little Savy really loved being with her too.

My mom had retired a couple of years earlier and loved retirement. After several years of therapy, she seemed healed from my brother Braden's traumatic passing when he was in his twenties. She managed to keep herself busy and got involved with volunteer work at the hospital. My dad was retired as well, but he spent most of his time on the golf course. He joined a senior men's league and was on the course several days a week. They both seemed to be happy.

When my mom arrived the next morning, I noticed something about her. She had been losing weight slowly, which seemed good at first, but her diminished size was becoming very noticeable and not in a positive way.

She didn't look healthy. Her eyes appeared to be sunken, and her skin color was pale.

"Mom, what's going on?" I asked. "Are you on a diet or something? You have been losing weight for months, and it is very noticeable."

"Just not that hungry these days, I guess." She shrugged it off.

Was she keeping something from me? Had she seen a doctor lately? I decided to ask her.

"When was the last time you had a check-up?"

"Haven't had one in years, to be honest. I do think it is time that I go. My energy level isn't what it used to be. I know I am getting older, but I literally drag myself out of bed in the morning now. My appetite is gone, and my clothes don't fit at all. They are all too big."

"Okay, that's it. Please call your doctor today and schedule an appointment to see him."

It felt like role reversal. I was playing the parent to my mom, but I felt it was necessary.

As I drove over to Carol's, I reflected on the last time I was at Savy and Carol's home. It was after Savy's funeral. Carol had invited family and close friends back to her home, where she held a reception.

It was a challenge to be in Savy's home again as the memories of him were everywhere. The photos, the awards, the smell of his cologne. Savy wore a special cologne that he bought when he was in Rome, Italy. It wasn't a common scent, but it was lovely. I wasn't familiar with the name of the cologne, but I do know it was easy on the nose.

Carol and I had a good visit, reminiscing and talking about Savy's favorite places, sitting in the garden he loved, but we didn't come up with any additional ideas beyond what we had spoken about on the phone.

After I left and drove away, suddenly, I could smell Savy's cologne in my car. This must be what they call a memory smell. I had read about memory smells. Essentially you remember an event from the past, and a scent will come to you as an actual memory.

The scent of Savy's cologne lingered, and it became stronger. I started to look around the vehicle to see if there was something else inside the car. There was nothing.

Was this strong smell another way for Savy to communicate with me from beyond? I decided to take it as a sign. Savy was sending me another message to let me know he was with me. It felt like a confirmation that I was on the right path.

"Okay, Savy, got the message," I said softly. "I'm here for whatever you wish for me to do."

Chapter 4

Benny was out the door every weekday by 7 a.m. He was consistently early to work. He liked to get an early start on his day before he found himself in back-to-back meetings. One of the things that I loved about Benny was that he never compromised his family time and did his utmost best to be home for dinner every evening unless he was traveling.

Little Savy was sleeping through the night now and would go to bed at 9 p.m. and wake up around 8 a.m. It was blissful finally to be getting a full night's sleep. The pediatrician said Little Savy was waking up often because he was hungry, but now that he was eating baby food, he was more fulfilled and slept for longer periods of time.

Benny was off to work, Little Savy was still sleeping, and the phone rang. I wondered, "Who in the world is calling at this hour?" as I crossed the room to solve that mystery.

"Good morning," I answered with energy in my voice. I was feeling extra enthused this morning as I had an amazingly deep sleep where Savy briefly entered my dream. He was frequently showing up in my dreams, usually for just a moment, but each time it felt like I was connecting with him.

"Sophie, it's Mom."

"Hey, Mom, what's up? It is awfully early for you to be calling. Everything okay with Dad?"

Dad had been having some heart challenges and was seeing a cardiologist. They were diagnosing the issue to determine how to fix his irregular heartbeat, low energy, and lack of breath.

"Dad's fine. It's me."

My heart skipped a beat. I felt a sinking feeling in the pit of my stomach.

"I went to see the doctor, and he ran some tests and believes I have lung cancer."

She was having a hard time getting the words out of her mouth. I could tell she was on the verge of tears but probably didn't want to alarm me. She was doing her best to maintain her composure.

At the same time, I was doing everything in my power to keep it together. I felt an overwhelming feeling of fear come over me, the fear of the unknown when it came to a cancer diagnosis. But I couldn't let that overpower me or her.

"Mom, everything is going to be fine. It's good you decided to investigate further. They have advanced treatments for lung cancer now, and if they catch it early enough, the chances of recovery are good. Have faith and only focus on perfect health in every part of your body. Does this inspire you to quit smoking now?"

My mom had been a smoker for many years. She tried different techniques to quit, like the nicotine patch, nicotine gum, and hypnosis, but none of those methods produced the results we were hoping for.

"Don't even think about asking me to quit now!"

I thought of the affirmation that Savy gave me when I was diagnosed with cancer, and I asked my mom if she would be open to trying affirmations. I repeated the affirmation that helped me to maintain focus during my treatments to show her what I meant.

I am so happy and so grateful that there is only perfect health in every part of my body. I choose to move mentally from my head to my toes, setting up a positive, healthy vibration. Every molecule of my body is vibrating in perfect harmony with all the good I desire. It is so. Thank you.

She came back with a calmer, almost accepting voice, "Sophie, I appreciate your positive attitude, but the doctor believes the cancer is in both lungs and doesn't believe it is operable. I am meeting with him next week to discuss the next steps and the prognosis."

"When is the appointment? I am coming with you." I didn't ask if I could come; I told her I was going, and I would ask Benny to stay with Little Savy or I would bring him with us.

"Okay, but Dad wants to come, and I believe Brandy too . . . and maybe Clancy and Allison as well." Her voice trailed off.

I realized at that moment that everyone in the family knew but me. I wondered why I was the last one to hear this news, but it wasn't the time to be thinking of myself. It was time to focus on Mom.

After I hung up the phone, I started to think about life without my mom. That type of thinking wasn't going to serve me, and I knew it. *Instantly I wanted to speak with Savy.*

Little Savy woke up, and it was time to direct my distracted attention to his needs: change his diaper, get him dressed for the day, give him his bottle, feed him baby cereal, and then go to the park.

The day was busy as always, and by the time the evening rolled around, and Little Savy was in bed sleeping, I was exhausted. It was one of those evenings when you feel like you will fall asleep before your head hits the pillow. Benny had been helpful all evening with dinner and the baby, and he told me to go to bed while he finished the dishes.

Minutes later, I was deeply asleep and in full-on dream mode. In the dream, I was with my dear friend Savy. We were sitting on our favorite park bench. He had appeared to me in a few dreams before, but only briefly, and we had not had a conversation. But this dream was different.

"Savy, you're here!"

"Well, of course, where else would I be?" he responded with a smile.

I was dreaming, and I was very aware that I was dreaming, but it was so vivid that it felt real. In the dream, I could see his presence. It was as if I could reach out and touch him.

"What's up, Sophie? How can I help you? You seem to be distraught. What is troubling you?" Savy asked.

"My mom's been diagnosed with cancer. It sounds ominous, and I am quite concerned. My relationship with my mom is so good now. She's happier now that she is retired. She has this special bond with Little Savy, and I love her being around. She also said that she and my dad have repaired their delicate relationship. It is the first time in my life that she seems happy, and now this!"

Savy gave that expressive tilt of his head that I so recognized.

"Sophie, you must understand that life is a precious gift, and no one knows how much time they really have. Death is not an ending. Death is simply a transition of energy."

"Hold on, Savy. Sorry to interrupt you. You have such depth to your wisdom that I sometimes need a moment to understand your thoughts. You said death is not an ending. What does that mean? If my mom dies, she's gone, that's it, that's all. I see that as an end. How is that not an ending?"

Savy looked at me perceptively as if assessing what I needed to hear.

"Death is not an ending. It may be a physical presence ending, but the soul lives on. And, if that invites your curiosity, then the next thing I am about to share with you may be a blockbuster. Death is a gift."

"Death is a gift?" I repeated in confusion.

"When someone you loves dies, they haven't left you. They have moved on to the next part of their eternal journey, but they are still with you in thought. All you must do is think of them, and you will be connected to their energy. You are connecting right now with my spirit. How do you think this is possible?"

"I don't know. You are the first dead person that I have connected with," I answered.

"It's because you have the *desire* to know. You have been eager to have this connection, and all you did was think about having it. You gave your attention to the desire to connect with me, felt intense emotion, and my spirit responded to your emotion."

What he said was true. I had longed for a connection.

"You are a soul, Sophie. You don't *have* one; you *are* one. Your mom is the same. Your mom moved into her body, and she will move out of it. Nothing is either created or destroyed. Therefore, there is no such thing as death. The soul or spirit lives on. As we start to understand this, then we handle death in a totally different way. Why are we joyous when somebody moves into a body as a new baby and then so upset when they move out of it? Well, it is because we lose the physical part."

"That's just it, Savy. They're gone."

"I don't believe anyone is ever *gone*. You can still communicate with them. You communicate through thoughts and feelings. Remember, spirit is omnipresent."

It was the middle of the night, and suddenly the dream was interrupted by the sound of loud thunder. I woke up with a start. I was breathing heavily and perspiring profusely.

"Are you okay, honey?" I had woken Benny up.

"Yes, my love." I touched his arm and lay back down. "I was dreaming about Savy again, only this time it was very vivid. We were having a deep conversation about life and death. We were sitting on the park bench just like we used to. I told him about Mom."

"Did you get any information on that mysterious project he wants you to finish?" Benny asked.

"We didn't get to that. We were talking about death. Savy said that death is a gift, but he didn't explain how it's a gift. I want to go back to sleep to get back to the dream," I said half-jokingly.

Moments later, we were back asleep. The dream did not continue, and I woke up in the morning with more questions than answers, hoping to reconnect with Savy's spirit again to dive deeper.

I had lost my brother and then Savy, and now I might lose my mom. I needed to understand how to cope with death and with the grief of losing those I love. *I needed Savy.*

And the thought popped into my head that Savy needed me as well. He trusted me to finish a project that he had left unfinished, something that he said would be the most important project of my life.

Chapter 5

Mom was surrounded by family as we sat with her in her doctor's waiting room. Dad, my sister Brandy, brother Clancy, sister-in-law Allison, and I sat there impatiently waiting to be called in for mom's prognosis meeting. As we waited, no one said a word. It was eerily quiet.

Mom was looking down at her clasped hands and appeared pensive. I wondered what was going through her mind.

In the last couple of days, Savy hadn't returned to my dreams. I wondered if I was trying too hard, perhaps even forcing him to show up in my dream so that I could continue the previous conversation. I wanted to know what he meant by "death is a gift." Death certainly didn't feel like a gift to me.

Savy always recommended looking for the blessings in every situation, no matter how adverse or undesirable. I asked myself, what was the blessing in Savy's passing? What was the blessing in my brother Braden's passing? I was hard fixed to find the answers, but I took a deep breath and decided to open my consciousness to possible answers.

Mentally I made a note of the blessings that came to mind. One blessing with my brother Braden's death was that he passed away without suffering. Following Braden's car accident, the trauma team discovered an advanced brain tumor that was inoperable and the type of cancer that would spread quickly. By dying as a result of the accident, he didn't have to suffer a painful decline or go through potentially aggressive chemo treatments. Was that a gift? I guess so. Another gift could be that since Braden donated his organs, he saved many other people's lives, including Savy. Savy received Braden's heart, and if it wasn't for Braden's heart, Savy may not have lived another ten years.

Okay, I was beginning to feel that I was on the right track with this *find the blessings* way of thinking.

With Savy, he knew he was going to pass, and this gave him an opportunity to say his *goodbyes* to those he loved. He wrote me a letter before his passing and instructed Carol to give it to me after he passed on, which she did. Plus, Savy lived way beyond what the medical professionals were casually calling his *expiry date*. The doctors declared that the new heart had given Savy another decade of life. Without that heart transplant, Savy wouldn't have made it to the new year, so the timing worked out perfectly for him.

Reflection turned to gratitude. I was grateful to have my brother Braden in my life for the period that I had him. I was also grateful for Savy, his wisdom, and our exceptional friendship.

"Angelina, the doctor will see you now." The nurse announced it was mom's turn to go in. "You can all go in with her. We've added a few chairs."

One by one, we filed into the doctor's office and took our seats. The doctor was already sitting in his chair behind the desk.

"Lina, I see you have your entourage with you," Dr. Pilsen said with a smile.

The doctor seemed to have a warm demeanor, and I hoped it was because he had good news for us.

My mom's given name was Angelina, but very few people called her that. Most people referred to her as Lina. Dad often called her Angel, and since their marriage seemed to have improved, he had started calling her *his angel*. It was sweet, to some degree, but I knew of my mom's pain from my dad's infidelity over the years, and I don't think any kind words or name-calling was going to release him from his guilt or the damage he had done. My mom said she forgave him, but I knew she was still hurting deep down.

"Lina, I love that your family is here and surrounding you. It will help you go through the next few months since it's important to have a support system."

Before the doctor could continue, impatiently, my dad jumped in to ask, "Doc, is she going to get over this? Will she be healed?"

My dad's voice was shaky. I was surprised by his visible display of emotion.

The doctor held up his hand for patience, turned away from my dad, and directed his attention to my mom. "Lina, the type of cancer that you have is called SMLC, which stands for Small Cell Lung Cancer. It is the most aggressive form of cancer. It typically starts in the center of the chest with your breathing tubes, the bronchi. This type of cancer starts with small cells that grow rather quickly and create large tumors. You now have large tumors in both of your lungs, and based on the imaging, they are inoperable."

Holy shit! This doesn't sound good at all. I had a feeling it would be bad, but I didn't expect it had gone this far. I turned to look at my mom. She was staring directly at the doctor with wide eyes. I looked around the room, and everyone else had their mouths open in stunned surprise.

The doctor continued. "We could try chemo, but it would be an advanced treatment and would make you very sick, and you will lose your hair. The challenge is that it may or may not extend your life. There certainly wouldn't be any quality of life. Surgery is not an option, and, at this point, radiation would be ineffective."

"Do you have any questions?" he asked gently.

Well, there is the question of the year! I had lots of questions, but it wasn't my doctor's appointment. I wanted to give my mom a chance to speak with the doctor while I maintained my composure in a support capacity.

My mom spoke first. "With treatment, how long do I have? And, without treatment, how long would I have?"

Oh my God! Am I hearing this right? I was in a state of disbelief. I realized that there didn't seem to be much hope. It wasn't a matter of *if* she was going to die; it appeared that it was a matter of *when* she would die.

"I would understand if you decided not to take any treatment, Lina. It will make you very sick, and it may not be the way you want to end out your life. Ultimately there isn't a cure for what you have. The cancer is too aggressive and has spread too far. I would say, realistically, you may have six months to live. I would suggest you get your things in order."

We all sat there in silence, absorbing the news. Finally, my mom stood up and said to the doctor, "Thank you, Dr. Pilsen. I appreciate your honesty. I don't want any treatment. I don't want any chemo."

She started to walk toward the door. Dr. Pilsen called out to her. "Lina, please book an appointment with the receptionist to come back in thirty days. I would like to keep a close eye on you and prescribe pain medication when it is time. And please call any time for an appointment. I would be happy to meet with you and your family."

We all piled in the elevator to go to the parking garage. No one said a word. I believe we were all shocked by the prognosis. When the elevator doors opened on the floor where our cars were parked, we walked out of the elevator, and Mom broke down in tears.

She crouched down to the ground and let out a cry that sounded as if it came from the depths of her soul. When she stood up, she seemed to turn her sadness into anger, and she looked at all of us and said, "Don't even think about asking me to quit smoking now! I am going to smoke until the day I die. It is too late now."

"We understand, Mom," I said. This was the consensus with all of us. There would be no argument on that.

"Mom, would you like us to come over and keep you company?" I asked. I worried whether Dad was going to stay with her or join his regular Wednesday golf league.

Mom spoke quietly, "I just want to go home and be alone for a while. I am kind of sleepy, too, and will likely take a nap. Let's get together as a family this weekend for Sunday dinner and bring the kids, too, please. I want to be surrounded by my family. My family is everything to me."

We all agreed to Sunday dinner.

Dad still looked stunned, but he helped Mom into his car to drive her home. Since everyone else came in their own cars, we all exchanged silent looks and then headed our own separate ways.

Once in my car, I immediately started to think about turning this potentially impossible situation around. I truly wanted to help her but wondered if she wanted my help. I decided that I would do more research and then present her with a holistic approach for dealing with this. Hopefully, she'd be open to a less conventional approach, especially if it could lengthen her life and maybe even improve the quality of it.

Benny had taken the day off and was home with Little Savy. Instead of driving directly home, I decided to take a detour and go to the park and sit on the park bench where Savy and I used to meet. I needed some quiet time by myself before I went home.

I parked my car in the lot adjacent to the park and walked over to the special park bench situated below the giant willow tree. That willow tree always felt like it was a shelter of some sort. It felt comforting to be surrounded by nature.

The birds were especially vocal that day. It was a beautiful, bright sunny day. Feeling pensive, I sat down on the familiar bench to reflect on the sad news about my mom.

A hummingbird suddenly appeared and began to flutter in front of my face. It was fluttering there as if it was perched on something. Hummingbirds always amaze me with the way they flitter and fly and hold themselves in position, almost like a helicopter. The little bird's presence got my attention and took my focus off the sadness. I couldn't help but smile.

Savy loved hummingbirds. He said they were the most fascinating of all the birds, and he said they can recognize humans. In the past, whenever Savy and I were having our regular park bench rendezvous, a hummingbird often would visit with us. This happened on many occasions.

Savy said that hummingbirds were loners like he was. I was somewhat of a loner as well. He said that, unlike other birds, hummingbirds didn't follow the crowd or the flock. They did their own thing. That was another one of the other reasons why Savy loved them.

Hummingbirds are also territorial and will protect their territories. The male hummingbird is intense and will fight fiercely if another hummingbird comes near or into their territory. The female hummingbird is similar in that she protects their nest. Kind of like a momma bear, I suppose.

Savy shared with me a funny story of a hummingbird feeder that he placed in his garden. He created this beautiful area; he called it his hummingbird sanctuary. He placed a hummingbird feeder, bird bath, beautiful plants, and a plaque that had two fake hummingbirds on it that looked rather real.

He said the plaque was placed in the bird sanctuary on a Saturday morning, and by Sunday morning, the two counterfeit hummingbirds were completely torn off the plaque and were lying on the ground. He assumed the hummingbirds did the damage as they wanted these trespassers to get away from their territory.

As I sat reflecting on my conversation with Savy, the hummingbird started to act in an unusual way. It almost appeared as if he were performing an acrobatic show. He stopped flittering in front of my face, took a sharp twenty- or thirty-foot ascent upward at a fast pace, and then stopped, flittered, and dove down toward the ground. I thought it was going to have a crash landing, but he stopped inches from the ground and came back and hovered in front of my face.

What in the world is going on? It was as if the hummingbird was trying to get my attention. It was mind-boggling.

And then I had a realization. Could this hummingbird be connected to Savy's spirit? What was the message he was trying to reveal? Perhaps it was to remind me to shift my focus immediately, away from sadness and over to joy. Maybe his message was to move my attention in another direction that could help my mom. After all, I was keen on investigating holistic approaches that could either save or significantly extend her life.

As soon as I had this realization, the hummingbird flitted in a circle around me and then climbed into the bright sky and disappeared.

The little mystery messenger was gone, and it was time to head home. Depending on what was happening at home, perhaps I could take an afternoon nap with my sweet Little Savy. The emotion of the day was heavy.

Chapter 6

When I returned home, I found Benny sitting at the kitchen table, working on some office tasks. Little Savy was having his afternoon nap. I told Benny about the doctor's appointment. He was saddened to hear the news about mom's prognosis and gave me a big hug. He said that we would be there for Mom. We would help her, support her, and do whatever we could. His kindness always shined through.

Since Little Savy was already napping, I didn't want to disturb him, so I went into the master bedroom to take a nap. As I was preparing to drift off into sleep, I spoke softly as if I was speaking with Savy's spirit.

"Savy, I know and understand that force negates. You taught me that. I have no intention to force you to communicate with me; therefore, I am relaxed knowing that your spirit will reveal itself to me. I feel a sense of being overwhelmed by my mom's prognosis, and I don't know what to do about the project you want me to finish. I would love to have further directions about how I should proceed."

I said those words with complete faith that Savy heard me and would respond, whether it was in my dream or some other way. Within minutes I drifted off to sleep.

"Sophie, I'm here." Savy's voice was like music to my sleeping ears.

This was the strangest experience. I was dreaming and knew I was dreaming. I could hear Savy, but I couldn't see him.

"Savy, what is the best way to connect with you? And was that you in the park earlier today as a hummingbird?"

"There are endless ways I can communicate with you. We are having a dialogue right now in your dream. This is one of the many ways. I have been communicating to you through physical items. Remember the handkerchief? I played a song in your car to let you know I was there. I brought the scent of my cologne into your vehicle to prompt you to realize I was there. I delivered a message via Louise, my spiritual advisor. Do you have a preference, or does this work for you?"

"Oh yes, Savy, all of that is true, and I am grateful. I would love to be able to communicate with you on demand."

"On demand?"

"Yes, when you were alive, if I wanted to speak with you, I picked up the telephone and called you. If you were available, you answered. It was easy. If you weren't available, I would leave a message and knew I would hear back from you. I didn't wonder if I would hear back from you. I knew for certain I would hear back from you."

"Expectation plays a big role in creating positive outcomes. We're doing that now, Sophie. You ask, I come. You want to connect, I get your message *in the field*, and I answer. This works perfectly."

"In the field?" I asked.

"There is an energy field where all thoughts reside. Your thoughts are energy in motion. I pick up on those thoughts and respond accordingly. Prior to my passing, I wrote you a letter. In that letter, I suggested that all you need to do is to think of me, and I am there. Simply imagine that I am in the next room, and if you want me to be in the same room as you, you can imagine it."

"It sounds rather simple. Is it really that simple?"

"It is. It truly is," Savy said with conviction. "There may be times when you think your mind is playing tricks on you. You may wonder if an event or a message is truly from me. To determine if it is a message from my spirit, use your *intuition*. It will guide you. And, yes, that was me in the park earlier today. I wanted you to know I was with you and to inspire you to switch from sadness to joy."

"I'm happy to hear that! I needed you, and you were there."

"Sophie, I want you to understand this, and please listen carefully. You don't need me. That's right, you don't. Everything that you need is within you now. If you trust that and understand that, all the answers you seek will be revealed to you. This is an evolved understanding."

Savy was kind, giving, and loving. I knew I didn't need him, but I wanted him. I loved that we were communicating. It was a miracle.

"Savy, it truly is remarkable that you are expanding my consciousness again . . . in my dream, no less! I do understand that everything I need is within me now. You taught me that when you were here in this physical world. But there are many things I am still learning and discovering, and I know you can help me accelerate the discovery. The purpose of a mentor or a guide is that they help get to the answers or get the answers faster, and that is what I desire. I want answers, and I want them now."

"Patience, patience," Savy said with a chuckle.

"You have a depth of understanding that is truly pure gold. Your experiences, your understanding, and your spirit are highly evolved, and as a result, I can gain such clarity and depth that might otherwise take me years to obtain simply by having a conversation with you. And now that you have passed on and reside in the eternal realm, I can garner an expanded understanding of what happens when we die."

"Believe it or not, I am still learning what happens," he said with another chuckle.

"Savy, you were my lifesaver when you were here on earth. I don't see it any different now, except now you are my angel. You are continuing to be a bright light in my life, showing me the way. The way to joy. The way to perfect health. The way to every outcome that I desire. There are some days that I pinch myself that I have been blessed with this relationship. To think the relationship didn't die when your physical body left this world is completely amazing and comforting to me. Thank you."

In the next moment, I was awakened from my dream by the sound of Benny and Little Savy playing and laughing. Little Savy was obviously awake from his nap, and it was time for me to get up from mine.

It was gratifying to me that I had such recall after these dreams with Savy. Prior to dreaming about Savy, I wouldn't remember my dreams. Now I remembered every word, and when I joined Benny and Little Savy in the living room, I shared all the details.

I loved that Benny never doubted that these dreams were real for me. I assumed he believed me. He never questioned it. He knew that I was benefiting from the connection.

The thing that I found strange about the dreams and communicating with Savy was that we would constantly get interrupted. Or the messages he sent me were cryptic, and I didn't always understand what they meant. Plus, I still had numerous questions to be answered, and I wasn't getting any closer to knowing what the special project was that Savy wanted me to finish. And what about Savy's comment that death is a gift? I longed for more clarity.

Patience, patience, Savy spoke softly in my ear.

"Oh my God, did you hear that, my love? Savy just spoke to me."

"The baby?" Benny asked.

"No, no big Savy, not Little Savy. I heard him say the words *patience, patience* in response to a thought that I had about getting answers faster."

I looked at sweet Little Savy. He seemed to be off in la-la-land again. He was smiling, giggling, and staring at something.

"Benny, look!" I said, pointing to the baby.

"Look at what?" Benny inquired.

"The baby is staring at something or maybe someone. He did this once before when he was in his swing. The only other time I saw him do this was when you were playing with him. It looks like he is watching someone, but no one is there. I think it is Savy . . . big Savy. Savy, the ghost."

As the words tumbled out of my mouth, I thought that Benny is going to start to think I've lost my mind. Maybe I had.

Benny looked at the baby and then looked in the direction Little Savy was staring. "He is staring at the television, but it isn't on."

My intuition kicked in. I grabbed the remote and switched it on.

The television was on the news channel, which was a rare event in our home. Benny and I rarely watched television, and if the television was on, it was usually on a sports channel. Benny loved watching his favorite sports teams.

In the exact moment that the television was switched on, the news anchor was in the middle of a story about Savy.

"The century-old property where the Sable Country Inn is located will be undergoing some major reconstruction. Apparently, billionaire Stephen Alexander Vaughan, who passed away earlier this year, bequeathed a rather large sum of money, according to some sources, into the millions, to restore the Sable Country Inn, a quaint property in the hills of the Benington Mountains."

As the announcer finished sharing this segment, the show went to commercial, and I switched the television off.

I looked at Little Savy and looked at the television.

"What was the significance of that?" I said out loud. It was more of a rhetorical question, as I wasn't expecting Benny to know.

Why would Savy leave a large sum of money for this run-down country inn? More importantly, why had my intuition led me to see that short news segment at that exact moment?

There must be a reason.

I had to put these clues together. Savy told me in my dream to trust my intuition. He told me to be patient when I asked for more clarity. Savy wanted me to see the news story about the inn. Does the inn have anything to do with Savy's unfinished project?

I think my angel from beyond has a strange way of answering my questions, but he may have just pointed me in the right direction.

Chapter 7

Sunday dinners at Mom and Dad's house were typically a joyous occasion. Mom loved to cook and bake, and she was great at it. Preparing delicious food was one of her ways of expressing the love she had for her family.

I believe it was her Italian heritage that brought that out in her. Her mom, my grandmother, was much the same way. Mom may not have expressed her love with words, but she sure did a great job expressing her love with food. I didn't understand this as a teenager, but I understand it now.

Mom wanted her entire family at her home every Sunday for dinner, but it wasn't always convenient for everyone to attend. But this Sunday, the entire family was there.

Lucie, Braden's wife, had remarried. Her new husband, Bill, was a welcome addition. He fit in well with the family. He was very boisterous and playful. Braden and Lucie's kids loved him, and we loved him too.

My nieces and nephews were older now and not as keen to come and hang out at their grandma and grandpa's home. I suppose they would rather be with their friends. Even though they were preteens and teens, they were very attentive to their cousin Little Savy and would play with him and entertain him. Little Savy loved the extra attention.

I wondered if we would be discussing Mom's prognosis at dinner. Benny and I had completed some research and had a list of potential holistic approaches for her type of cancer. We were ready to discuss them if she was open to it. We decided to wait for a suitable time to share our findings.

We all sat around the dining table, and Brandy announced that she and Steve had finally set a firm wedding date. They had been engaged for over two years but hadn't announced a date. Numerous times we asked them when the wedding was going to be, but they never had an answer. Now the blessed date was booked and firm. It was obvious that Mom was thrilled as she let out a loud "whoop" in response to the announcement.

I worried that the timing was perhaps a little inappropriate, but I was wrong about that. I believe their wedding now gave Mom something to look forward to and took the attention away from her health situation.

They decided to have a destination wedding and share their joyous event with immediate family and a few close friends on an island in the Bahamas in the Caribbean. I thought that was a rather bold decision considering the commitment required for guests to attend. It wasn't a wedding venue that one could just drive to, attend, and then drive home. This was a much bigger commitment both in time and expense.

I looked at Benny when they announced it was a Bahamas island wedding, and in unison, we both verbally agreed that we would be happy to go. I already knew that Little Savy was going with us too.

Brandy and Steve had been dating for ten years and living together for seven of those. I don't think either one of them wanted to have children of their own. They loved kids, and Brandy was great with kids, but they seemed to be into their careers and traveling more.

Perhaps they'd consider having children after they were married.

"All I want is for my children and grandchildren to be happy," Mom shared.

She had tears in her eyes as she said this. I wondered if Brandy's wedding was one of her dying wishes.

My dad had been attentive to my mom all day and helped where he could in the kitchen, which was unusual. He seemed to be making an extra effort to ensure that she had the support she needed, even if it put him out of his comfort zone.

That made me happy to see him step up and take more responsibility. She would need us all before long.

After the dinner dishes were cleaned up, we sat in the family room enjoying cappuccinos.

Clancy was the first one to speak about the so-called elephant in the room. I believe we were all a little fearful about bringing up Mom's cancer prognosis for obvious reasons, but Clancy had told me earlier that he wanted to find out if Mom had any dying wishes.

He spoke softly. "Mom, is there anything you'd love to do? Is there anywhere you would love to go? Anything at all?"

Mom took a quick glance around the room. It appeared all eyes were on her.

"All I want to do is spend as much time as I can with you, my family. There really isn't anywhere I long to go other than the Bahamas for Brandy and Steve's wedding," she said with a smile.

Mom said she would give it more thought as far as any other special wishes. It was obvious to all of us that her priority going forward was to be with her family as much as possible.

Brandy pulled me aside to ask if I would be her maid of honor. Of course, I said *yes*. Steve said his best friend Barney would be his best man. No other attendants were planned as they wanted to keep their wedding simple yet elegant.

Brandy turned her attention to Mom. "Would you like to go wedding dress shopping with me this week? I've already asked Sophie to be my maid of honor, and I was thinking of going to that wedding dress shop in town to check it out. I would love it if you joined us."

"Absolutely," Mom responded.

Benny and I decided to wait until everyone else left to talk with Mom about holistic approaches. By the time everyone left, Little Savy was asleep in the playpen in their guest bedroom. Mom had equipped her home with a highchair, playpen, and toys so that we didn't have to bring baby stuff with us each time we visited, other than diapers and a change of clothes.

I broached the subject of holistic healing with mom, but she stopped me before I could go much further. She wanted none of it. She said she wasn't interested in trying any experimental approaches to healing. She accepted her diagnosis and was going to make the best of the time remaining. Everything inside of me wanted to fight against her decision, but I knew that it wasn't up to me.

"Soph, since Little Savy is already asleep, and he looks so comfortable, would you mind allowing him to have a sleepover at Grandma's tonight, and you can come and get him in the morning?" Mom offered.

Benny loved the idea. "Thanks, Mom. That's very thoughtful of you." He gave me a boyish look that said he would not mind having me all to himself for one night.

I wasn't keen on the idea of a night away from Little Savy. As much as it was a lovely offer, I wasn't sure I'd be able to handle the thought that Little Savy wasn't going to be sleeping at home. Mom and Dad's place was only a five-minute drive from our home, and I knew that if I needed to, I could be over in a matter of minutes.

Reluctantly I agreed.

Mom sensed my hesitation and said, "If there are any issues, I'll call you immediately. Allowing Little Savy to sleep here is better for him too. He's already asleep, and he looks very comfortable. You don't have to wake him up, take him home, and attempt to get him back to sleep again. You can come over in the morning, and we'll have coffee together."

If this made my mom happy, I was going to be fine with it. She seemed to be quite excited about the idea of Little Savy spending the night. How could I possibly deny her any reasonable wish at this point?

When Benny and I got home, we went out to our outdoor summerhouse, made a lovely fire in the fireplace, and poured ourselves a glass of wine. It was a beautiful evening, and the moon was full. It was a clear night, and the sky was filled with stars. Despite Little Savy not being home, I was surprisingly relaxed.

We discussed the upcoming wedding and decided we would not only purchase Mom and Dad's airline tickets but also arrange first-class seats and upgrade their room so they had the nicest suite available. My parents had never flown first class. They hadn't been on an airplane very often at all, but we had enough points from all our years of traveling to easily upgrade all our tickets to first class.

We decided to make the entire experience first class, including limousine rides to and from the airport. We would incur all expenses and tell them to leave their credit cards at home.

At the thought of traveling in style, I remembered with a smile something Savy said to me years earlier when he was talking about choosing a luxurious lifestyle. He suggested always traveling first class. His refrain was *front of the plane, back of the car, front of the plane, back of the car*. He would repeat those words with great fervor and a touch of humor.

It wasn't long before the fire dwindled, and we decided to call it a night. We walked hand in hand to bed.

Lately, I had begun a ritual prior to drifting off to sleep where I would consciously encourage a visit from Savy. I didn't do this every night. There were some nights that I fell asleep so quickly that I didn't give it a second thought.

Tonight, as I drifted off, I asked for a visit. This turned out to be one of the most unusual nights that I had had since connecting with Savy's spirit. The dream that came was longer than any previous one, and one where Savy enlightened me in ways that gave me a new understanding of death and dying.

Chapter 8

Savy revealed himself almost immediately after I fell asleep. He was as real to me as he had ever been. I couldn't touch him, but I felt his presence and heard him clearly.

"Sophie, I know you are scared. I feel your fear and sadness at the thought of losing your mom. It is an earthly experience, and many humans go through this. However, if you knew what was *next*, you would only feel peace. Fear not, dear one. Your mom's soul will be enveloped in the most extraordinary and complete feeling of love. Words cannot effectively describe it. The everlasting arms of spirit will hold her when she leaves her physical body, and her spirit will move on to a heavenly place. Allow yourself to feel the peace of this *knowing*."

"Oh, Savy, I want to believe that."

"Nothing will sever the connection you have with your mom or any other loved one who has passed on or will pass on. Remember the concept of *one mind*? We talked about this before. You and your mom are forever united, and no one or nothing will ever break that connection. Your mom can be as close to you as she ever was, even when her spirit has left her physical body. You think of her, and she's there. Think of the air in one room and the air in another room. There is no separation of that air. Even though she may be in the next room, the air is the same that you breathe without question."

I understood what he was saying. The concept was so comforting that I had tears in my eyes.

"You have an unmistakable sense of connection with your mom, and that connection is with her soul or spirit. That will never be denied unless you allow it to be. And that deep connection will be just as evident when she passes as it is right now. Does this make sense to you?"

In the dream, we were transported back to our park bench, and we continued to speak in the same genuine way that we always had.

"Yes, it makes perfect sense, Savy. When we first met on this park bench years ago, you helped me look at things in a new way, with a fresh and healthy perspective. Your way of thinking hadn't been my way of thinking. Simply put, you were a positive thinker, and I was a negative thinker. Thankfully you helped me look at things differently, and my whole world changed. What you are sharing with me now is so unconventional, so different from anything I've ever heard before. And don't get me wrong, I love what I am hearing, but it may take me a minute to get my head around it."

"Do yourself a favor, Sophie, and get your *heart* around it."

"Hmm, that's interesting. What do you mean by *get your heart around it*?"

"Accept these ideas *emotionally*. If your intellect is in the way, you may miss some of the most valuable understandings of life and death. You're right that this way of thinking isn't conventional. I may not have been able to have this conversation with you when I was alive, but now that I am in the spiritual realm, my awareness has expanded, and I know I can help you significantly. For example, when I said that *death is a gift*. Would you love to know what I meant by that?"

"Oh yes, please, my wise Savy," I pleaded.

"What if I told you that death is the greatest thing that could happen to anyone? Please don't misunderstand me. I am not saying hurry up and die. The truth is that at the moment of death, the soul feels this incredible freedom, the most extraordinary sense of peace. The joy and love you will feel will be unlike anything you've ever known. Death is not an end but a new beginning. As odd as this may sound, death can be the happiest moment of one's life. It is almost impossible for me to explain or describe and likely improbable that you will understand."

He was right that I didn't understand. I was trying hard to turn off my head and wrap my heart around his words, but it was mind-boggling to think of death as the happiest moment of one's life.

"Have you ever watched or heard stories of people who have near-death experiences? What do they all say? They say that the experience was so profound and welcoming that they didn't want to return to their physical body. They felt love, joy, and peace. Many who cross over, and have the choice to return, don't return."

"Yes, I've heard about those stories."

Savy paused as if he was carefully choosing his next words.

"Many humans who pass on, prior to death, were afraid of death. People who are alive today live in fear of death. They are wasting their precious time while they are very much alive. Instead of living, they live in fear of death. That is no way to live, to really live. If they only knew what happens when the physical body dies, and the spirit moves on, they would never fear death."

Savy slightly shifted directions with his thoughts.

"There is another aspect of death and dying that is valuable to know, and this part affects the loved ones who are left behind. I want to share with you the negative and destructive impact of grief."

"Hold up . . . how is grief a negative emotion? Every human feels it. I thought it was a natural expression of an understandable reaction to loss."

"Yes, that is true. I am not sure every human feels grief, but many do. When a loved one passes, it can be devastating for some. The sadness occurs because of the *separateness*. They no longer see their loved ones, and they feel the loss. Most people are not prepared for this type of sorrow. Depending on the relationship with the person who died, that sorrow can be felt deeply and be so unexpected. People don't prepare for it and are not equipped to handle it when it happens."

"That sadness is certainly what I felt when I thought I would never be able to talk to you again," I confessed.

"Death is inevitable for everyone, Sophie. When people are living their so-called normal life, they are not planning for the loss of a loved one. There isn't much thought that goes into that, but they do prepare a will or secure life insurance so the financial aspects are taken care of. But they don't prepare emotionally for death."

"Oh, geez, Savy, you are blowing my mind here."

"I get it. I really do. This will likely blow most people's minds, but it is important. It is important we understand this and, more important, that we implement it too. People who prepare for the death of loved ones will infinitely suffer less. This doesn't mean you won't miss them; it simply means that you go through the experience in a much healthier way."

Savy let me think on this for a moment before he continued.

"Life isn't always easy, smooth, or a bed of roses. Adversity is something that every human will experience at some point in their life. Some experience it more than others. The more prepared you are for it, the easier and faster it will be to get through it. Uncontrolled grief can be devastating for the living. It can cause sickness, poverty, and destruction. This type of knowledge isn't taught in schools. Most people are unprepared and therefore suffer greatly, and it is unnecessary."

Savy was on a roll, and I was happy to be learning from him again.

"All emotion demands expression, whether it is a positive emotion or negative emotion. If the emotion isn't expressed, it becomes *suppressed*. Suppressed negative emotions turn from un-ease into disease."

Savy paused to assess whether I was in alignment with his message. "Do you understand this, Sophie?"

"It's a lot to take in, Savy, but I think I do."

"We are only just beginning to scratch the surface of this understanding. I want to enlighten you so that you can enlighten others. This is the reason why I chose you, Sophie. You have this insatiable appetite for knowledge, and you love sharing it with others. Your passion is to make a positive contribution to millions of others. Your heart is pure. I sensed that from the moment I met you. I am sharing this with you because I know you will help many people. I specifically chose you to complete this important project because I know you'll follow through. I know you'll understand the significance of what I want you to do, and I also know you'll not only complete this project, but you'll do it better than I could have ever done it."

"Thank you, Savy. I am so grateful for your faith in me. You haven't told me what it is you would like me to do. What is the project?"

"Not so fast, dear one. I know you want to know, and I know you are ready to dive in, but there is more for you to understand before you can begin. If I told you now, the result wouldn't be as effective. There is something else that you are going to go through that will elevate your consciousness to the point of conviction, and then you will be truly ready."

I began feeling frustrated. "Why is it that just when I feel that I am about to have a breakthrough in understanding what you want me to do, I feel more confused?"

"Allow me to explain it this way. If you wanted to build a house, would you grab a hammer and nail and begin construction? No. Why not? Because you don't have the design. You haven't seen the outcome, the bigger picture. You aren't yet clear on what the end looks like. How can you begin until you gather everything you need to complete the project? That is what we are doing here. You are being prepared."

"I'm being prepared?"

"Trust me, Sophie. You will understand in due time. Remember what I suggested before: *wait as the one who understands*. Assume you do understand. Relax in the knowing that it is all very clear to you now, even if it isn't. Remember also that *infinite patience produces immediate results*. Do not allow yourself to feel frustrated. Everything is unfolding exactly as it should. Trust that. All will become crystal clear to you at the perfect time."

"Sounds like backward thinking to me," I said with a chuckle. "I say that humorously, Savy, but I do understand what you are saying. It makes sense because of the things you've taught me in the past. You've shared wisdom with me before, and I simply increased my faith. That is what I will do now."

"Yes, feel the faith, Sophie. Be full of faith. Be the source of faith. Be the source of good. Be the source of patience. Be the source of love. Be the source of kindness, compassion, and gentleness. Further guidance will be revealed to you while you are building unwavering faith."

That was the end of the dream.

I woke up in the morning feeling so calm and peaceful. I grabbed my journal and began to write. I wanted to capture the entire dream on paper before it left my consciousness.

Savy had said that there was something else that I had to go through to be truly ready to take on his project. He didn't say whether this would be something positive or negative. I had to trust and build faith and wait to find out.

Chapter 9

For the next two months, almost every night, Savy came to me in my dreams. He shared ideas and unconventional concepts that were sometimes surprising but always deeply intriguing. He shared, and I absorbed. It felt like I was in school again, studying, learning, expanding the boundaries of my knowledge, and intensifying my understanding of the truths that Savy shared. Unlike when I was in school, the subject matter was important to me and interested me. I also believed what I was learning would be helpful to others.

As I had done with all my Savy wisdom sessions, I absorbed his teachings with a grateful heart. Savy was guiding me to the most unique yet powerful understanding of life and death intertwining all around us.

"Make no mistake, Sophie, you will use this knowledge in a way that will positively impact the lives of millions," Savy told me during one of our sessions.

I still wasn't aware of what he meant by *positively impacting millions*, but I was waiting *as the one who understands*. I knew that he was going to enlighten me at the perfect time with further direction on his unfinished project.

I remembered Savy quoting Solomon years before: *in all thy getting, get understanding.* Savy fed my insatiable appetite for understanding.

In the meantime, my mom's health was slowly deteriorating. She began to experience some pain, and her doctor prescribed low-dose pain medication to help. She was taking frequent naps and continuing to lose weight. She considered purchasing a dress for Brandy's wedding but decided to leave it until the last minute as she wasn't sure what size she would be wearing by the time the wedding came around.

Mom would make frequent visits to our home to invest time with Little Savy, or if she wasn't feeling up to leaving home, we went to her. It was beautiful to observe the love she had for him. I captured memories by taking videos and snapshots. I was already feeling sadness at the thought she wouldn't see Little Savy grow up.

When I told this to Savy, he invited me to turn my thoughts of grief to thoughts of gratitude. He talked about grief being a selfish experience. At first, I felt a bit insulted. But he wasn't insulting me at all.

He explained, "People express pain, either emotional or physical, for *attention*. They may not intentionally or consciously look for attention, but they receive it nonetheless. That attention becomes an addiction. People become addicted to emotions. They aren't even aware that they develop a habit of attention-getting and become completely unaware of the destructiveness of that practice."

I had to admit that his words rang true, and I didn't want that to be me.

"Sophie, my suggestion for you is to rise above feelings of grief, and you will not only feel better, but you will also be an inspiration for others."

Savy must have sensed how difficult this discussion was for me because his next words were gentle.

"No one is immune to the experience of loss. We will all experience loss because every person born will die. Death and birth are universal and natural. Grief, even though it is understandable, will never bring someone back to life. Grief also will not bring anyone comfort."

"Okay, I get that," I said, "but how do we deal with grief in a healthier way when grief hits us?"

"By first understanding that you cannot change the *cause* of the grief. We simply change our *reaction* to it. Change the reaction, change the effect. It is the thought of loss that makes one sad; therefore, change your thought. You can control your thoughts."

Mentally I repeated that statement to make it take root: *We can't change the cause of grief; we simply change our reaction to it.*

"Most people are not thinking mindfully about what they are thinking. However, with *mindfulness* of our thoughts, we can choose to switch to a new thought, a happier thought. The thought of the gift of life. The thought that you had that person in your life for a period and the many gifts that came along with that. Do you see where this is going? Remember when you were so distraught because your boyfriend Chad ended your relationship? You were grieving because you experienced loss."

"Oh yes, I remember it very well. I was feeling so much grief that I wanted to end my life. Thankfully I met you, and you invited me to change the way I was thinking and to focus on the great things in my life. Of which, there were many. That change of focus changed my life. In fact, I believe it saved my life."

"By doing that, you lessened the pain, and eventually, it went away. Do you feel grief now for the loss of that relationship with Chad? It is a rhetorical question, as I know the answer. Let's look at it this way, if you were to focus on the blessings from Braden's passing, what would they be? Or, better yet, let's shed some light on the event that is unfolding in your life right now, the upcoming loss of your mom. This may be a delicate topic at this time, but would you be willing to share with me the blessings?"

Even though I was in a dream, the emotions were very real. "I don't know if I am ready to go there."

"Go where?" Savy asked with genuine concern.

"Go to the idea or thought that my mom is going to die,"

"Sophie, she *is* going to die. And so are you. So is every other living person. It is inevitable. People shy away from this subject because they begin grieving even before the event has occurred. The act of grieving *before* an event happens is a complete and utter waste of time. Grief, as we discussed earlier, is destructive. Do you not think that your mom's prognosis is a gift?"

"I'm not sure, but I think I'm ready to think about it."

"Many people do not get the opportunity to *say goodbye* to their loved ones. Most people do not get the chance to *fulfill their dying wishes*. This is not the situation for your mom. She is fulfilling her dying wishes and investing more time, quality time, with her family. She thoughtfully bought all her children and grandchildren beautiful cross necklaces to remember her by. Oops, maybe I shouldn't have revealed that," Savy said sheepishly, as if he had just given away a secret.

"It is okay, Savy. Mom told me she was buying cross necklaces for her children and grandchildren. She asked me to help her find them. I get your point. I really do. I remember very well focusing on the great things in my life, and I even created a GIMY journal, which I carried with me everywhere. It completely shifted my old way of thinking. I can see how that exercise could significantly help me right now too. Thank you for reminding me."

"It would serve all people to *focus on the gratitude and joy* our loved ones bring us or have brought us. This way of thinking and feeling becomes a way of living and thriving. This is the way to healing as well."

"Savy, your words are like a breath of fresh air. Your wisdom is serving me now."

"Did you have any doubt?" Savy asked in a joking manner.

"It wasn't that I had doubt. I lacked awareness. I was behaving in a way that most people behave—grief-stricken without realizing the potential damage it was doing."

"Sophie, have you heard the expression that time heals all wounds? The truth is that it doesn't necessarily heal all wounds. Some people choose to reimagine a traumatic event repeatedly. They relive it over and over. They bring it back to life every time they think about it, talk about it, grieve over it. Time will help heal, but *only when the individual shifts their way of thinking and chooses to find the blessings.*"

"You say time heals all wounds, but you told me once that time doesn't really exist. It's nothing but a measurement in a man's mind. I'm not sure I understand the contradiction."

"Yes, that's true. There really isn't any such thing as time because all we have is *now, this very moment*. You can be healed in this moment. The healing depends on whether you accept this truth now or at some time in the future. I would suggest you accept it now and save yourself a lot of time. If you mull this over in your mind, it will make perfect sense."

"That sounds like homework," I said with a laugh.

"I am going to say something else that I'm going to invite you to accept as a loving idea because it *is* a loving idea. If you accept the fact that your mom is going to die and choose to heal your grief *now*, before she dies, you will help your mom. This is a very unselfish act."

"Whoa! Just when I think I've got what you're saying all figured out, you throw out a curve ball, and I'm confused once again. My mind is going all over the place. Are you saying that I can feel healed from the grief of her loss before my mom even dies?"

"You're not confused at all, Sophie. Yes, that's right. Simple yet not necessarily easy. *Lift your spirits, and you will lift your mom's.* Feel gratitude and express it, and you will find more things to be grateful for."

I suddenly felt an energetic shift in my emotions toward my mom's situation. I grew excited at the thought that I could better help my mom get through her challenge by not letting grief consume what time we had left. I could support her by feeling gratitude for her being in my life. I had the choice to thrive and heal beyond grief and loss.

"Oh, wow, I get it, Savy, I really get it, and I believe the whole world needs to hear this."

"Yes, Sophie, you are accurate on that. I understand your publisher asked you to write another book, and I believe you will. I have the perfect name and subject for that book, which will lead you to make a positive and beneficial contribution to the lives of millions. It will be called *Understanding: The Gift of Life and Death.* This book will be a huge success, far greater than your first book, and will sell for years."

"Yes, it feels so right, Savy. Thank you for guiding me to such a wonderful idea."

Even as I basked in the positive energy of Savy's encouragement, I had another thought.

"Is this the project you said you wanted me to finish?"

"It is definitely a project you will complete, but it isn't the one that I personally started and desire you to finish. Let's save that discussion for later when you are ready."

It was mind-blowing to think there was a whole other project for me to pursue in addition to writing and publishing a book.

"My head is full, Savy, and I don't think I can absorb any more. Can I wake up now?"

Savy chuckled. "Yes, dear one. Wake up and do your homework."

Chapter 10

The limousine arrived on time to take five of us to the airport, including me, Benny, Little Savy, Mom, and Dad. It was time for our trip to the Bahamas for Brandy and Steve's wedding. Heaps of excitement loomed as the family was geared up to have some fun in the sun. Brandy and all the others were already at the resort getting things organized. They flew down two days earlier.

Mom was unaware of the limo, the first-class airline tickets, or the penthouse suite we arranged for her and Dad, so when we showed up to pick them up in a limo, they had surprised looks on their faces. It was precious to see. Benny had his camera out and was snapping photos left and right.

"I have never been in a limo in my life!" Mom exclaimed as she slid her way into the back of the vehicle. I had no idea that she had never been in a limo. I assumed everyone had been in a limo at some point in their life. I had traveled by limo numerous times, especially with Savy. He had his own driver and would often travel in a limo. Savy said he loved to travel that way so that he could relax or get some work done. He was a serious multitasker and made the best use of his time.

It felt so wonderful to do these special things for Mom. Benny and I had the biggest smiles on our faces.

When we got to the airport, we went to the priority line to get checked in for our flight. Mom was surprised again. She turned to me and said, "Soph, this line is for the first-class passengers. We can't stand here. We must go over there." And she pointed to the regular check-in line.

"We are all flying first-class, Mom."

"What? How can . . . ," her voice trailed off. Mom knew enough not to ask any questions. She smile as if she had a realization. I loved that she accepted the gift without questions. If the situation had been different, she might have been uncomfortable with this special treatment, but I could tell that she understood why we decided to travel this way.

After we received our boarding passes, we went to the first-class lounge to wait until our flight was called. The lounge was spacious and had comfortable seating, a large buffet of food, and beverages of all sorts. And it was all complimentary. Mom looked like a little kid in a candy store. Her eyes were open wide, and she was smiling ear to ear.

It was so heart-warming to see her taking it all in. She deserved this celebrity treatment. Dad seemed to be into it as well.

I knew that mom's prognosis wasn't only impacting her. It was impacting the other members of the family, too, but mostly Dad. Dad had some health challenges of his own. His heart wasn't functioning as it should. The medical professionals had discovered blockages in his arteries. He had already undergone surgery when they implanted a stent in his artery. He was also a smoker, and the doctors said that the smoking contributed to this. Like Mom, he wasn't ready to stop smoking. He felt that smoking calmed his nerves, and maybe it did, but it was doing more damage at the same time.

In my dreams, Savy was helping me understand the grieving process, and I was being equipped to handle it, but my other family members weren't. I decided I would help them if they were open to it.

Even though we were heading off to this fun destination as a family, I was anxious to get to work on the project Savy wanted me to finish. I decided to give the project my complete attention once we returned home.

It wasn't long before our flight was called, and we were boarding the plane. Mom, Dad, Benny, Little Savy, and I were all settled in our first-class seats. We had an entire row in the first-class section. Mom was loving every minute of this. She was fascinated by the large-screen televisions in each pod. She was playing with the buttons and checking out all the goodies the flight attendants had left on the seats.

The flight attendant began offering champagne and orange juice. Mom wasn't much of a drinker, and she was taking pain medications, but she graciously accepted the glass and signaled for us all to toast Brandy and Steve.

Little Savy was already napping in the baby carrier that Benny had over his shoulders. I decided to attempt to sleep on the flight since I was up very early that morning and late to bed the night before. Secretly I was hoping to have a conversation with Savy as well. For me, champagne was like a sleep aid. I am certain the plane was still on the tarmac, and I was fast asleep.

Savy joined me in my dream on the airplane.

"Sophie, may I remind you to enjoy the moment?"

"What do you mean? I am enjoying myself."

"You may be from time to time, but your energy is shifting from where you are to elsewhere, and I sense your unsettledness. I get your messages *in the field*, as you know, and I understand your desire to focus on the special project. But you have other priorities right now, and I want you to be fully absorbed in the *present moment*. These moments with your mom and family are precious and will create lasting memories. Enjoy every minute. Savor them. Does that make sense to you?"

"Perfectly. Thank you, Savy."

As fast as the dream began, it ended when Little Savy woke up and wanted his mommy.

This was Little Savy's first flight, and, thankfully, he was calm. Having a baby was easy on the airplane with four adults to share in the caring.

The flight seemed to go quickly, and everyone watched out the window as we began our descent over the sparkling, cobalt-blue waters. There are thirty inhabited islands in the Bahamas. We were about to land on the island of New Providence.

After we landed and cleared customs at the airport, we walked outside to find a local gentleman in a black suit holding a sign with Mom and Dad's names on it. He was our limo driver who was hired to bring us to the luxury resort. Mom saw the driver and the sign and turned to me and gave me a thumbs up. She seemed to be adjusting to this luxurious lifestyle quite well. Savy would be proud.

When we got to the resort hotel, I directed my parents to the VIP guest services desk to check in. Their suite was known as the Owners Suite, and it was the nicest accommodation at the resort. My parents had their own butler and a fridge stocked with a wide variety of drinks. Their oceanside balcony went across the entire width of their suite to enjoy the magnificent view.

We arranged to meet the rest of the wedding crew for an early dinner. It was during this dinner when Mom gave every family member a small, gift-wrapped box.

Inside each box was either a yellow gold or white gold cross necklace. They were each uniquely designed and beautiful. Mom said that this was her way to be with us always. There wasn't a dry eye around that table as we gratefully received these special treasures.

The days leading up to the wedding flew by so quickly. The weather was wonderfully warm. We loved being able to wear minimal clothes and enjoyed not having to get dressed up in coats and boots to go outside, especially with the baby.

Little Savy loved the kids' pool area and play structures and enjoyed playing in the sand. We would do activities with him all day, and by the early evening, he would be exhausted and easily go to sleep. We were exhausted as well. Most evenings, Benny and I stayed in our room to be with Little Savy, except for the day of the wedding.

The magical day arrived, and everything went off without a hitch. Brandy looked stunningly beautiful, and she was radiant with happiness. Mom had found a beautiful gold gown, and she looked like a million bucks. She was the slimmest I had ever seen her. It was the first time in my life that my mom, Brandy, and I were all the same weight.

It seemed like we had just arrived, and it was time to start packing to head home. Mom and Dad had a magical time. I think the trip exhausted Mom to a large degree, but she was not showing her fatigue. Whenever we suggested an excursion, she was the first one to say, "Yes, let's do it." She was on board with any activity going on. Dad too. At one point, I thought the trip was going to bring Dad to his knees, as he looked more exhausted than Mom, but he never complained.

On our last evening, Dad had a few too many after-dinner drinks. Benny took Little Savy to the room to put him to bed, and Dad and I went to the lounge chairs beside the ocean. Mom had also gone to bed early that evening.

"Sophie, thank you for doing this for Mom and me," Dad said with a shaky voice. I immediately thought he was going to cry, and I wasn't sure if I would end up joining him.

I thought this moment might be the best opportunity for me to share some Savy wisdom on grieving. Instead, Dad began to talk about the guilt he was feeling for the way he treated Mom in the early years of their marriage.

"Dad, the past is the past. You can't change it. Mom has forgiven you, so you need to forgive yourself. Let it go. Holding onto guilt will only destroy you. It will not serve you."

Dad sighed deeply.

"You are being great with Mom. You are completely loving and caring, and it shows. You are attending to her every need. We all appreciate you for this. You are here for her, and she appreciates you so much. Mom told me that she has no regrets. She also said she is at peace with the past, so you should be too."

After my words, Dad broke down and cried. It was extremely awkward for me as he was my parent. I told him everything was going to be okay, but I knew that we were in for a challenging time. The doctor had given Mom six months to live, and we were about to head into the home stretch. It wasn't the time to talk about the grieving process as he was heavily under the influence of alcohol, but I knew that Savy's wisdom would prove beneficial at the appropriate time.

The trip home was as seamless as the trip down. Little Savy slept the whole way. Traveling first class certainly made traveling much more enjoyable.

We brought back wonderful memories and lots of videos and pictures showing the whole family playing, laughing, swimming, and lounging in the sun. There was one special photo of my mom in her tropical bathing suit and a big floppy hat. I decided that I would have it printed and keep it by my desk. I wanted that carefree memory to last a long time, maybe forever.

Once we were home and fell back into our regular routines, I decided it was time to ask Savy if we could focus on the project he wanted me to complete.

I was hoping that the time I had spent in my dreams with Savy, absorbing his wisdom from beyond, was the *something* that he said I had to go through to be truly ready.

It was time to find out.

Chapter 11

We had been home for a couple of weeks, and Savy had not entered my dream even once. I was discouraged and began to wonder if he was ever coming back. I couldn't imagine not being able to talk to him again. I pushed that negative thought away and kept trying to reach him.

I tried a variety of approaches, including demanding him to show up. That didn't work. I did a ritual of welcoming him into my dream, and that resulted in nothing. I tried meditating to relax before going to bed, and that didn't work. I tried positive affirmations, but no Savy. Nothing seemed to produce the desired results.

The longer this went on, the more frustrated I became. I looked for signs all around me of Savy communicating with me, and I didn't see, hear, or sense anything.

Several more days passed, and I was experiencing anxiety and starting to question the previous sessions that I had with him. Maybe I made it all up. Perhaps it didn't even happen, and I only imagined it did. After a few moments of self-doubt, I assured myself that there was no way I had imagined making a connection with Savy's spirit.

If Savy wasn't willing to talk to me in my dreams, there must be a reason. Was it a test of some kind? Maybe he wanted me to do the work on my own. But where do I start?

I asked Benny for advice. "What should I do? I have no idea what this project is. Savy did tell me that I would be writing a new book about what he's teaching me called *Understanding: The Gift of Life and Death*, but he specifically said this was not the special project. I don't know what to do now. Any ideas, my love?"

Benny had this exceptional gentleness about him, especially when he gave me advice. "Honey, I think you are trying too hard. You are attempting to force the situation, and that never works. You taught me that, and Savy taught you. Go back to the basics. What did Louise tell you? She said that you would receive more direction once you went to *his favorite place*, right? Focus on that as your next step."

"Oh, my goodness, you are so right. Thank you. Great suggestion," I replied. "I will do that." I was a woman of action, and not doing anything wasn't sitting well with me.

Meanwhile, Mom's health was starting to deteriorate rapidly. The doctor increased the dosage of her pain medication, and she was sleeping often. The health care system arranged for a nurse to visit Mom daily. Little Savy and I would visit her often, but she slept through most of our visits. If she was awake, it would only be for brief periods. Dad stayed with Mom around the clock. He was attentive to her every need. I was amazed at how he continued to step up and put her needs first.

As a family, we stayed true to our habit of Sunday dinners at Mom and Dad's place, but it was me, Allison, and Brandy who did all the preparation and cleanup. The guys helped as well. Even though Mom was sleeping a lot, she expressed her gratitude for all of us being with her as often as possible.

We registered Little Savy for a baby playgroup three mornings a week, and he absolutely loved it. I wasn't sure if he was going to be fine with me leaving him at first, but he took to this playgroup like a fish to water. He loved the stimulation of the group play and enjoyed being with other babies and toddlers. This gave me the free time to explore some ideas for tracking down Savy's favorite place.

The first morning Little Savy was at the playgroup, I drove to the park where Savy and I used to meet. I sat on the familiar park bench beneath the willow tree, ran my fingers across the weathered wood, and closed my eyes. Silently I spoke with Savy. No response. I spoke to him out loud. Nothing. I wanted to burst into tears out of frustration but stopped myself. Exasperated, I drove home without any connection with Savy's spirit.

When I arrived home, I called Carol. I asked her if she would be okay with me coming over the next morning. She told me that I was welcome any time.

The next morning, after dropping Little Savy at his playgroup, I drove over to Carol and Savy's beautiful house. I explained to Carol about the lack of communication from Savy and that I needed to figure out his favorite place to receive further directions.

Mentally I had made a list of what I thought might be Savy's favorite place, including the park bench, his library, and his bird sanctuary area in his backyard.

Carol invited me to roam their home and go anywhere my heart desired. When we went into Savy's library, I sat in the large wingback chair that Carol told me he preferred. It was one of two big comfy chairs on either side of the fireplace facing the floor-to-ceiling bookshelves. This chair felt so comfortable that I understood why Savy enjoyed reading there.

Carol started a fire in the marble fireplace and told me to take my time. She slipped from the room, and I sat down to connect to the energy of Savy. I closed my eyes and imagined we were communicating. I waited several minutes, but nothing happened. I opened my eyes and looked around the room. Maybe I would see a clue, but nothing stood out for me. I did enjoy looking at the titles of all the books that Savy read and talked about, and that made me feel closer to him.

After an hour of sitting in the library, I got up and went outside. Carol showed me Savy's preferred outside spot, and I sat down on a comfortable outdoor chair and closed my eyes again. I took in some deep breaths. I quietly waited and waited and waited.

I stood up and stomped my feet. "What in the world, Savy! What do you want me to do? Where do I go? I am so frustrated!" I turned and noticed Carol standing at the window, looking in my direction. I don't think she could hear me, but she was probably wondering what I was doing. I smiled and waved at her.

I felt completely bewildered. I was genuinely at a loss. Benny was right, though. I was trying too hard, and perhaps a little *letting go* might go a long way to helping me calm down.

I thanked Carol for her hospitality and got in my car to pick up Little Savy, and then we were off to Mom and Dad's for a visit.

After dinner that evening, Benny asked me if I would be open to going on a date night with him. I was pleasantly surprised by his invitation but pleased as I knew it was important for us, as a couple, to have some alone time. So, of course, I accepted and decided we would get a babysitter on Friday night.

Mom was the only person who had ever babysat Little Savy. Benny reminded me of how easily Little Savy adapted to the playgroup and that he would likely be fine with a babysitter. Besides, he was in bed most evenings by 8 p.m. and slept through the night. I was quite certain Benny was right, but I wanted to have the perfect babysitter.

I called my niece Lilly, who was a responsible straight-A student and a mature teenager. I had also observed her with Little Savy at Mom and Dad's, and she seemed to be great with him.

Friday night arrived. Lilly came over early and started playing with Little Savy. He was already fed, bathed, and in his pajamas, ready for bed. He wouldn't be going to sleep for another hour, but all she had to do was give him his bottle and put him in bed. I told her that I would call later and check in with her.

Lilly was quite calm and delighted to spend this time with Little Savy. She told me that she was going to do some homework after he was in bed, so there was no hurry for us to return home. She brought her pajamas and planned to stay the night. Benny was quite excited about the opportunity for the two of us to have this time together, but I was feeling anxious.

Once we were seated at the table at our favorite restaurant, and after a glass of wine, I was starting to unwind. As parents of a baby, we didn't usually get to eat so leisurely, and it was delightful just to chat and laugh and enjoy our five-star meal. Just before our desserts came, I called the house and spoke with Lilly. She told me that Little Savy went to bed without any problem, and she was working on her homework. All was well, and I relaxed even more.

Since we were having dinner at our favorite restaurant, which had also been the venue for our blessed day, Benny and I reminisced about our wedding. We were having one of the best evenings we'd had in a long time. It felt so relaxing, so peaceful.

Suddenly, I heard the words *the inn* in my mind, and I let out a gasp. Savy's favorite place immediately burst into my consciousness.

"Benny! I know where Savy's favorite place is. It is the Sable Country Inn! Remember when we saw that news segment a while back? Savy left millions of dollars for the restoration or renovation of the inn."

"Wow, that's great, honey. I knew you would figure it out. Are you going to go there? I don't work tomorrow, so you can go if you want, and I can stay home with

Little Savy. I would welcome some quality daddy-son time."

"Oh yes, my love. That is exactly what I am going to do!"

I had to laugh at myself. I had been trying too hard, looking anxiously everywhere except in the right direction. And the clue had been there right under my nose.

I also had to wonder whether the words *the inn* came up from my subconscious working diligently in the background, or did my dear Savy grow impatient with my slowness and whisper them to me?

Chapter 12

I got up early on Saturday morning to spend some quality time with Benny and Little Savy before heading to the Sable Country Inn. I decided to leave after Little Savy went down for his morning nap. Benny was excited about investing some quality time with his son, but I was sorry to leave. I loved my weekend time with Benny and Little Savy. It was our precious family time.

After assuring myself that I would be back in a few hours, I hopped in my car and began the hour-and-a-half drive. It was a spectacular sunny day and a perfect day for driving. As far as this little outing was concerned, there wasn't a plan in place. I wasn't going to meet anyone, and I honestly had no idea what I would find. I was open to anything.

The drive was easy and smooth. When I pulled into the laneway for the inn, I noticed the perfectly groomed and manicured property. It was obvious that this place was loved and cared for. I was already wondering about the reason for Savy's generous gift. I was expecting a run-down place, and it was anything but.

The green and lush grounds were spectacular, and the closer I got to the main building, a nineteenth-century-style country house, the more impressed I was. The four-story structure was solidly composed of brick with stone accents and white trim.

I thought the news report said that this place was undergoing renovations or restoration. It didn't look like it needed any restoration, or maybe the work had already been completed. Whatever the story, it was impressive.

As I pulled up to the columned portico entrance, a smiling young man waved me over to where he was standing. He was the valet, and once I stopped, he opened my car door and offered to park my vehicle. I thanked him and walked through the large glass entrance doors to enter the building.

I literally stopped in my tracks as I took in the splendor and charm of this place. It was, by far, one of the most beautiful and classy lobbies I had ever visited. The entrance was elegant yet welcoming and gave off a positive vibe that made you feel immediately at home.

A young woman in a well-tailored black jacket with a nameplate approached me and asked if she could help me get checked in.

"Oh no, I am not a guest of the inn." At that point, I wasn't even sure what to say. I think I was still reeling by the beauty of the place. I did not expect the inn to be so stunning. I sincerely thought that the place was going to be run down and perhaps even uninviting. It was everything but that, and because of the unexpectedness of the quality, I was somewhat speechless.

The young woman asked if there was anything she could help me with.

"I am just looking around," I responded. I didn't know what else to say. In my mind, I was considering telling her about Savy's *messages* but felt that she might think I was loony.

"Would you mind if I took a look around the property?"

"Yes, of course, you may. Please let me know if I can be of service. If you have any questions at all, you are welcome to ask any of the staff. You will find them wearing our corporate colors of black and gold, and they all have nametags on their uniforms. Any one of the staff would be delighted to assist you. After you take a look around the building, you are welcome to check out the hiking trails into the woods or beside the lake or golf course. And, of course, you are welcome to have lunch in our five-star restaurant."

She had been attentive, friendly, and welcoming. I thanked her and started walking around in a daze.

I strolled freely, taking in the magnificence of the lobby, restaurants, pool area, gift store, and bar. There was gentle classical music playing, ever so softly, and very few guests in view. It felt so calming. I wondered if they had spa services as it looked like the perfect place to go and unwind and relax.

I happened to come across some construction at the end of the building, and it appeared that they were adding a new section. I wondered if they were adding more rooms or perhaps a conference area. I was surprised at how quiet it was, considering there was construction going on, but I suspect it was because the addition was far from the main lobby area.

"What am I doing here?" I asked myself.

Unexpectedly I heard a voice behind me. "How may I be of service?"

I turned to see a young man walking up behind me. I must have looked surprised as he said, "I'm sorry. I didn't mean to startle you, but I heard you say something."

"I was talking to myself," I said with an embarrassed giggle. "I tend to do that sometimes, only I usually do it much quieter."

"What can I do for you? Are you a new guest of the inn?" he asked with a warm smile.

I glanced down at the young man's name on his nametag.

"Thank you, Jim, but I honestly don't know what you can do for me, and no, I'm not a guest of the inn. I came here, and as crazy as this may sound, to see if I could get some answers."

"Answers to what, may I ask?" Jim looked sincerely curious.

"Well, it may take me a minute or two to answer that, and I really would like to talk to someone. Do you have a few minutes?"

"Yes, of course. We have some ongoing construction at this end of the building and no place to sit. Let's go and sit in the lobby where it's much more comfortable."

I followed Jim back to the lobby, and we sunk onto one of the incredibly comfy brown leather sofas.

I wasn't ready to tell a stranger about having conversations with a dead man's ghost, but I did share the story about losing a dear friend and receiving a message from him through his spiritual advisor. That at least sounded a little more believable since many people believe in psychics.

I told Jim the message said that my friend wanted me to finish a project that he had started, and it was important for me to go to my friend's favorite place to find answers. I told Jim that I thought Sable Country Inn might be that place.

Jim listened as if he was hanging on to every word. When I finished, there was a moment of silence.

Jim broke the stillness by speaking first. "Was your dear friend, by any chance, named Stephen Alexander Vaughan?"

To say I was surprised is an understatement. "How did you know that?" I exclaimed.

"Savy was my grandfather."

"Seriously? Wait, I thought you looked vaguely familiar. I saw you at Savy's funeral. Now that I think of it, I have also seen photos of you at your grandparents' home. You were much younger in those photos, though."

"And you are Sophie. My grandfather spoke of you often. He loved you like a daughter. He had three sons, including my dad, but you were as important to him as any of his children. Do you know why Savy wanted you to come here?"

"He said for me to get answers, but I don't know the right questions to ask to get the answers I need."

Jim nodded and seemed to ponder my words for a moment.

"Savy came here often to work on his business ideas and goals. He loved this property and told me he had big plans for this place. We never rented out his private suite, as we kept it for him so that he could come here at a moment's notice. No one has been in it since he passed away. Would you like to see it?"

"Oh, yes, please. Do you mean now?"

"Yes, of course. Follow me, and we'll get the key from the front desk."

I walked with Jim to the front desk, and he introduced me as *Savy's special Sophie* to every staff member we encountered. It was clear that the staff loved Savy. Many of them also seemed to be familiar with who I was as well. That was interesting.

Jim gave me a quick tour before we went to Savy's room. On the way, he showed me the library Savy had built for the inn. The library was very similar to the one Savy had in his home, with wall-to-wall books ascending from the floor to the ceiling.

We got in the elevator, went to the top floor, and walked to the end of the hallway. The inn was four floors high, and according to Jim, there were two one-bedroom suites on each floor and twelve regular single rooms.

Jim unlocked and pushed open the double doors that entered the magnificent and opulent suite. The main room had a large u-shaped sofa with a marble wood-burning fireplace. Above the mantle was a framed painting of the lake where Savy lived.

Next to the window sat a mahogany desk with a leather swivel chair. There were papers sitting on the desk. There was a larger oval table that could accommodate eight people. I wondered if Savy ever had meetings here. It was as if Jim read my mind because he said that Savy actually loved working at the bigger table. He said that Savy would spread out his papers on the table and occupy the entire space.

The bathroom had a large soaker tub in the corner with a separate shower that had multiple jets. There were double sinks, and both the floors and towel racks were heated. The towels looked thick and lush. I wanted to bury my face in them.

The bedroom had a king-size four-poster bed, and facing the bed, was another marble wood-burning fireplace. No doubt, Savy preferred wood-burning fireplaces to gas, as he had several wood-burning fireplaces in his home as well.

"Wow," I said softly as I walked around this lavish suite.

The windows were floor-to-ceiling and wall-to-wall. The view was exceptional as it looked out over the entire manicured gardens. The blinds on the windows were remote-controlled, and with one button, you could move them up or down.

After the quick tour of the suite, Jim and I came back to the main living room. Jim told me how much Savy loved this place. I could now understand why it was his favorite.

I glanced down at the desk and was surprised to see a manila folder that had my name on it. I pointed to the folder and asked Jim, "What's that?"

"I'm not sure," Jim said as we both drew closer to the desk. He picked up the manila folder, and we both read the words on the front. *TO REVIEW WITH SOPHIE* was written in bold letters across the folder.

"I guess this is for you," Jim said as his hand extended the folder in my direction.

"What is it?" I asked.

"Perhaps you should look it over."

When I opened the folder, I discovered architectural designs for a facility of some sort. There were several documents and pages of handwritten notes. I started to flip through them quickly until Jim suggested that I take the folder home with me and bring it back at another time.

"Would you be okay if I did that?" I wasn't sure I should remove anything from Savy's room.

"Sophie, this was obviously meant for you. Please take it and come back next week, and if you like, bring your family, and you can stay here, right in Savy's suite."

"That would be wonderful. I would love to do that. Perhaps I can bring my husband and son with me next weekend, and we can stay at the inn for a couple of days. I am more than happy to pay."

"You will be our guest. We are happy to have you and your family any time."

Then it dawned on me that Jim may have to get permission for me to stay there. "Don't you have to get approval for that from the manager or the owner?"

"I am the manager, Sophie, at least for now. I can confidently say that you can stay here as our guest," Jim said with a smile.

Jim is in charge of this inn? Amazing. He seemed so young to be running an establishment such as this, certainly not much beyond university age. It wasn't my place to question. I thanked Jim for his kindness and headed to my car.

My head was still reeling as I began the drive home. I had finally found Savy's favorite place. It struck me that Carol hadn't considered the inn when we were brainstorming.

She said Savy kept his work stuff to himself and that he would sometimes go away to work on projects so he could concentrate. The inn must have sounded like a workplace rather than a favorite place.

I looked forward to telling Carol that I had solved the mystery or at least part of it.

Perhaps the manila folder I was carrying home would provide some additional clues about the unfinished project Savy wanted my help with.

Chapter 13

On the drive back home from the Sable Country Inn, I had this incredible desire to pull over on the side of the road and go through the folder that Savy had left with my name on it. I was wildly curious to know about the contents and very intrigued to learn why my name was written on the outside of the folder.

Patience had never been my virtue, although I was open to being more patient and intuitively understood how valuable patience can be. There is a depth to understanding the importance of when to act and when to allow things to happen versus doing nothing at all. I was a woman of action, and Savy knew it. I believe it was one of the reasons why we were kindred spirits. We were both driven to produce results.

I often felt challenged with not acting when I was *waiting as the one who understands*, which meant practicing and activating faith. This was a wise Savy teaching that I was taking to heart. Savy's spirit had also been communicating the word *patience, patience* to me on recent occasions.

I also recalled a time when Savy told me that *unsuccessful people hope things are going to happen while successful people make them happen.* Savy was the latter, and he taught me to be the same.

These two philosophies pull in opposing directions. The trick, Savy said, is finding the balance between them and discerning when to act and when to wait in faith.

I pulled my vehicle into the garage and, once parked, raced into the house. With great anticipation, I was looking forward to seeing my sweet little baby and my handsome husband.

Little Savy and Benny were in the backyard playing on the swing set. When Little Savy saw me walk outside, he let out an adorable little squeal, smiled the most glorious smile, and extended his arms in a gesture for me to pick him up. I picked him up, spun him around, and kissed his sweet cheeks a dozen times. Oh, how I loved my baby. Benny wrapped his arms around us both in a big hug.

I excitedly described the details of my trip that day to Benny and told him that I was going to review the folder after dinner. He offered to bathe Little Savy and put him into bed so that I could dive in early, and even though I really loved doing those things, I was looking forward to getting started on learning what was in the folder. I also knew that Benny enjoyed his precious time with Little Savy.

After dinner, I set myself up at the dining room table and opened the folder. Inside I found an abundance of valuable and surprising information. There were plans for an entirely new section for the inn, a recommendation for a name change, a marketing plan, financial forecasting, expenses, budgets, and a detailed description of Savy's vision. The concept seemed extremely well thought out.

One of the first surprising things I noticed was the recommended name change. Savy suggested changing the name from The Sable Country Inn to *Sophie's Magical Inn* with a tagline of *A Special Place for Positive Transition, Transformation, and Change.*

This proposed name change invited more questions. Why would he recommend calling this place with my name? What did I have to do with the inn? Why did he choose the word *magical* as part of the name? Savy had never spoken of this place, not even once. His grandson

Jim told me he was managing the inn, yet he didn't seem to be aware of the folder or its contents.

As I continued reading, I saw that Savy's radical vision for the inn was totally unlike that of a standard vacation destination. It was obvious that he felt the inn could be a sanctuary, a magical place for people at certain crossroads in their lives, from those who desired to break through old limiting beliefs to those who were about to transition into the final phase of life.

Those people who were about to transition into the next phase of their eternal journey could go, check in, and share the last days of their lives with their loved ones. At the same time, they would receive proper medical care in an environment of serenity. Savy's vision included the highest level of hospice care available anywhere on the planet. As revolutionary as it was, Savy's vision made perfect sense to me because the place truly had a magical, serene feeling about it.

One of the things that I discovered in Savy's notes was a special consideration for the families of the people who are about to transition. There were already places in the city that offered palliative care and hospice settings, but none of them offered facilities for the patient's loved ones to stay, certainly nothing as beautiful as this. This new version of the inn and the new addition would accommodate those families in a beautiful, serene setting.

That part of Savy's vision would require around-the-clock medical professionals to be on staff. I am certain he had considered this substantial expense, as he did have a spreadsheet with the financials on it. Once I reviewed the vision, marketing strategy, and outline, I would review the financials last.

His vision also included an entire wing for personal transformation for those who wanted a new lease on life or desired to move beyond old limiting beliefs. He listed various treatments, curriculums, and strategies that could be followed for the guests to experience their transformation or quantum leap within a relatively short period.

Regular guests could also simply stay and enjoy the facilities, but Savy's vision seemed to be directed primarily at those who were genuinely ready for a positive life shift or positive experiences.

He envisioned the inn maintaining the same luxurious lifestyle while adding a meditation room, a yoga room, a visualization room equipped with virtual reality tools, a bird sanctuary area, improved and expanded gardens, and special trails going into the woods on the hundred-acre property. The entire facility would be wheelchair accessible, including the trails in the back of the property. I wondered if he envisioned the trails being paved or simply nicely groomed. Standard spa treatments would also be available for massages, saunas, facials, and the like.

Everything about this new version of the inn would be designed to create an emotional, life-altering, uplifting experience, whether the guests were coming there to end out their days or to experience a renewal or rebirth. Savy suggested having positive affirmations on posters with awe-inspiring images. In addition to the extensive library, he also wanted to furnish each suite with reading materials that would uplift and inspire.

Customer service would be second to none. Similar to the ratio of staff to guests on a cruise ship, he proposed a one-to-two ratio whereby there would be one staff member for every two guests in some capacity or another to serve at the highest standards.

The most magnificent vision and the place where Savy's heart really shone through in his plan was the section where he wrote about honoring gifts, almost like scholarships, to those who wanted to stay at the inn but didn't have the funds to pay for it.

The part that caught my interest was the palliative section. It appeared that the new version of the inn would have a special place for anyone who was about to transition to death. This struck me because of the stage my mom was getting to. I wondered if she would like something like this, and if she did, how could the environment be created that would give her the most peace? I decided I would share this with my parents to get some insight into the wishes of someone who was about to go through such a phase.

After investing a couple of intense hours going through the contents of the folder, I was eager to discuss it all with Benny. Benny said he could easily see the link between this inn and me, especially since I was at a point in my life when I was considering what would be next in my career.

"But Benny, we live an hour and a half drive from there! If Savy intended on having me run it, where would we live?" I asked with genuine concern. I loved our home, and I loved being close to my family, especially with my mom going through her health challenge.

"Don't be concerned about that right now. Why do you assume he wants you to run it? Maybe that was just a name he liked to use, Sophie's Magical Inn, while he was working out his ideas and vision," Benny offered.

"Okay, if that's true, why did he write "TO REVIEW WITH SOPHIE" on the folder? Was he just going to ask me about it to get my feedback? I have a strong feeling it was more than that."

"I think you're right. Go with your instinct. Trust that you will be guided. Isn't that what Louise said?" Benny reminded me.

"Yes, absolutely. I have my connection with Savy in spirit, and now that I know about his vision, I am confident I will receive further instructions or guidance as we dive into this. Besides, we're going to the inn next weekend to stay in Savy's suite. I can speak with Jim and get some additional insight from him."

The thought entered my mind to invite my parents to come with us, but I wasn't sure if my mom would be up for the trip. Since the next day was Sunday, and we planned to have dinner with my parents, I decided to ask them to join us next weekend.

When we arrived on Sunday, my mom was sitting in the lounge chair in the living room, sucking on a popsicle. She looked the best I had seen her in a long time.

"Mom!" I called out. "You look fabulous. How are you feeling?"

"Feeling good. The last couple of days, I have felt much better. Yesterday Dad and I went for a little walk outside, and it was so refreshing to breathe in some fresh air. I feel good today too. Let's hope this keeps up. It was starting to depress me, being stuck in bed every day."

She went on. "I wanted to contribute to our Sunday dinner, so I asked Dad to go to the store and get the ingredients to make my upside-down pineapple cake, and he did. Guess what we are having for dessert tonight?"

Mom was grinning with the biggest smile. I sensed her pride for having the strength to bake a cake.

"I will admit, though, that I had some help. Dad helped me mix the ingredients and put it in the oven. I napped while it baked, but there was nothing for either one of us to do while that was occurring."

Since Mom was in good spirits and seemed to have more energy, I felt there was no time like the present to suggest the weekend adventure to the inn for next weekend.

Mom looked at Dad, he looked back at her, and they nodded their heads in agreement at my offer. I decided I would call Jim and request an extra suite as my mom and dad were going to join us.

Chapter 14

As I laid my head on my pillow, I gave thanks for such an amazing weekend. There was so much to be grateful for. I had found Savy's favorite place and learned about his amazing vision for the inn. Mom was looking better and appeared to have far more energy. I wondered if she may be heading into remission. It was possible. Patients go into remission all the time, and it could happen for her.

No sooner was I focused on my *gratitude* that I was off into a wonderful sleep, and the dreaming began.

It had been a long time, but Savy was back in my dreams.

"Savy! Where have you been?" I felt immensely relieved.

"I've been right here, Sophie. You were trying too hard to force me to show up, and as you may recall, force never works. Force negates. The more you try to make things happen, the less likely they will. It's a universal principle. You do remember that, right?"

"Yes, I sure do, and I knew I was getting in my own way. I found myself in a hole and didn't know how to climb out. Benny reminded me about the negatives of attempting to force as well. I'm grateful for the lesson and even more grateful you're back. I have questions for you."

"Wonderful, as I have some answers for you," he said cheekily.

Savy had the most wonderful sense of humor, and even in spirit form, it shined through.

Several questions flooded my mind, and I wasn't sure where to begin. *What should I ask first?*

"Sophie, I can read minds, you know," Savy said in a matter-of-fact way.

I began to chuckle. "Savy, I would love to know more about your thinking behind the Sable Country Inn, the name change, and my involvement. Can you shed some light on the folder of information you left on your desk in your suite, please?"

"Yes, of course. I've been waiting for you to ask. Years ago, I discovered the Sable Country Inn and fell in love with the place. I loved the beautiful building, the accommodations, and the surrounding property. I always felt good whenever I stayed there. My best and most prosperous ideas came to me when I was there. Inspiration for businesses or business improvement ideas came to me when I walked the trails or sat outside. I loved the gardens, the lake, the scenery, the wildflowers, the birds, the other animals that roamed the property like the chipmunks, raccoons, squirrels, deer, foxes, coyotes, and the bears."

"Wait! Bears? There are bears there?"

"Yes, black bears, but they don't hurt anyone if you don't bother them. The Sable Country Inn was founded by a couple of monks many years ago. They became elderly and couldn't take care of it, and offered it to me to buy, so I purchased it. They agreed to stay on for a while until I could find a suitable replacement. My grandson Jim is trustworthy, mature for his age, and a nurturer, and he agreed to run it for me temporarily."

That certainly confirmed my assumptions about Jim.

"Jim has put off going to med school until his replacement has been brought on. He promised me he would stay until the perfect person took over. I told him that I had someone in mind, but first wanted to see how you felt about the idea, the environment, and the opportunity."

"Med school? Jim is going to be a doctor?" I asked.

"Jim's passion is healing people. Yes, he is going to be a doctor. He wanted to be a doctor when he was a little boy. He received a little doctor's kit when he was three years old, and he seemed to lean toward being a doctor and has never deviated from his goal. His father, Stephen Jr., my oldest, is also a doctor."

"You never spoke about your children when we were together. Why not?"

"Never felt the need. When we were together, I would focus on serving you. It never felt important or relevant to talk about my family. Typically, if you recall, our conversations were about recommendations on how to live a better life. More specifically, I focused on guiding you through your life challenges and offered advice to help you with your goals."

"I'm so grateful that you helped guide me."

"Sophie, I came to truly believe in you. Your beautiful, loving, giving, generous heart was transparent to me. It was blatantly obvious that you have the spirit of service too. It is a natural way of being for you, as it was for me. I built my businesses on that premise of serving. When I was alive and preparing the plans for the inn, there was no other human being that I felt was better equipped to run this place than you."

There it was. He did want me to run the inn. I was glad that was clarified. After reading Savy's vision, I already knew that I wanted to do this. That was very clear to me, but I didn't know how to make it happen logistically. Plus, what about my mom?

Savy picked up on my thoughts and responded.

"Next weekend, you have plans to go there. Do that. Enjoy it and connect energetically to the place. Walk around the grounds. I understand you are staying in my suite. I am happy Jim made that recommendation. I also understand you are taking your parents. That is a wonderful idea. I am confident they will love it too."

"That's what I'm hoping," I responded to Savy's words of encouragement.

"Take your time, Sophie. Review the plans that I put together. If you feel inclined to change them or modify them in any way, please do. I only started working on this during the last year of my life. Even Jim doesn't know all that I had in mind. All ideas are open for modification. If you do have any changes to the new extension, now is the time to make them, as the construction has begun. They anticipate the new wing to be completed within the next two months."

"Oh, two months isn't very long. I'll need to go over the plans in detail."

"Go to the inn and stay there as often as you wish. There is no urgency as far as your decision is concerned, although I feel very strongly you will accept this new role. I genuinely feel it will be the most important work you will ever do. Everything in your life has led you to this moment. One of the greatest benefits you will find is that you will be a part of something truly magical. This will feel elevating for you. This is truly treasured work. And, writing the book on *Understanding: The Gift of Life and Death* will brilliantly compliment your work at the inn."

Treasured work. That was the inspiring thought I remembered as the dream ended.

When I woke up in the morning, I shared the dream with Benny over coffee. He listened intently. He had a grin on his face as I spoke, so I had to ask him, "Why are you grinning?"

"Honey, you are the one with the direct line with Savy, but I absolutely, wholeheartedly knew where this was going. I felt it intuitively. There was no doubt in my mind. I look forward to going there. I have a feeling we're going to have a magical weekend at Sophie's Magical Inn." He said this as his smile grew big.

"Sophie's Magical Inn, huh? I do like the sound of that. It is an inviting name. Okay, well, let's see how things unfold on the weekend, and we'll take one step at a time."

With that, we gave each other a high five, and it was time to get Little Savy out of bed.

Chapter 15

The following Friday afternoon, our bags were packed, and we were on our way to the inn to stay for the weekend. There was excitement in the air for what we might discover and experience.

Mom had another good week and was continuing to feel better. She visited her doctor on Monday, and he sent her for more tests to determine whether the cancer had progressed since the last time they checked. The doctor was pleasantly surprised and pleased to see Mom feeling and looking good.

Oddly enough, Dad was looking a bit ragged. Perhaps caring for Mom was taking its toll on him. A weekend away was something that they both needed and would benefit from.

As we pulled into the circular entranceway at the inn, I saw Jim standing at the doorway. *Was he there to greet us? How did he know we were arriving at that exact time?* I believed it was simply a coincidence that we pulled in at the precise moment he was standing there.

"Welcome," Jim said with a warm smile. "We are delighted to have you join us. Please leave your vehicle here, and we'll take care of it and your bags. I have already taken the liberty of checking you both in and have your suites ready for you."

"Thank you, Jim. Did you say suites?" It sounded like Mom and Dad were also going to be in one of the suites. I wondered about payment. I hadn't provided a credit card for check-in. I decided I would ask Jim about this later when my parents weren't around, as Benny and I were planning to cover all expenses.

"Yes, we have you, Benny, and Little Savy in Savy's suite, and your mom and dad will be on the same floor at the opposite end of the hall in another suite. I have also assigned a butler for you for the weekend, and I'll introduce you to George when we go inside. He can help book dinner reservations, schedule spa treatments, or get you anything you desire. Our restaurant has been designated as one of the finest in the world. We have an award-winning chef, and his dinners are second to none. Be sure to ask George to make your dinner reservations, as the restaurant tends to be booked up fast."

I turned to look at Mom, and she appeared pleased. It was obvious she was content to stay here. I had wondered if it was going to be too much for her.

Jim led the way into the lobby and introduced us to our butler George. He was an elderly man dressed in a three-piece suit and had a distinguished but friendly look about him. He spoke with a British accent and sounded as impressive as he looked. He wasn't wearing a uniform or the standard black and gold colors, and I wondered if he was hired specifically to take care of us or if he was a regular staff member. Either way, this was an incredibly thoughtful gesture on Jim's part.

George went with Mom and Dad to help them get settled in their suite. We confirmed that we would meet up with them in a couple of hours. It was time for an afternoon nap for Little Savy, and I wanted to meet with Jim to see if I could get some questions answered. Benny offered to stay in the suite while Little Savy napped. Mom and Dad said they were going to rest for a bit as well.

While everyone else relaxed in the suites, I met with Jim in his office. Jim's office was situated in a quiet corner on the main floor. Like the suites, the office had floor-to-ceiling windows that looked out onto the beautiful gardens. Everything about this place was tranquil and inviting. It wasn't long before I realized that the renovation and updates were all Savy's ideas. Jim was simply honoring his grandfather's wishes to complete the new wing while temporarily running the place.

"When do you plan to go to medical school?" I wanted to get an idea of the timing of Jim's departure and to determine when I would be needed.

"In three months," Jim replied.

I was surprised by his answer. "That soon?"

"Actually, it's been a year since I postponed starting med school at my grandfather's request. As he was approaching his final days, my grandfather met with his children and grandchildren individually. Savy told me how much he loved me and trusted me to take over the transition of the ownership of the inn. I gladly agreed as I could see how important it was for him, and I would do anything my grandfather asked."

Jim's words were somewhat surprising as I hadn't really considered who actually owned the inn since Savy's passing.

"Who are the owners of the inn now that Savy is gone," I asked.

"According to my grandfather's will, the Sable Country Inn is in the hands of a trust with a board of directors. Actually, that's all I know at this point. One thing I do know, Sophie, is that my grandfather intended for you to take over managing the inn."

I was pretty blown away by the enormity of the challenge of stepping into Jim's shoes and fulfilling Savy's wishes.

Jim asked me for my thoughts on running the inn. He wanted to know if I was serious and open to the opportunity. He added that the details of my compensation would be shared by the board of directors.

I hesitated before answering. I wasn't concerned about the compensation as Benny and I were financially set for life, but there was an important detail that I felt should be discussed.

My biggest concern with taking over the inn was my family. Benny had worked for the publishing company for many years. He had a great career and loved his job.

Also, Mom's prognosis wasn't good, and I wanted to be with her as much as possible. We also had a beautiful home that I loved and had never thought about moving until now. And my Little Savy was still so young. There were a lot of things to consider.

After a long discussion before we left home, Benny and I decided we were open to the idea of taking over the inn. It surprised me that Benny was so receptive to the idea when we had no idea how this would affect his work.

Perhaps Benny would decide to join me in running the inn. Maybe he could work remotely and stay on with the publishing house. That might be a possibility. Benny assured me that it would all work out perfectly. I was so grateful for the high level of faith he had for me and our family.

If Benny hadn't known Savy, it might have been different. Benny and Savy had a close relationship, and Benny never questioned Savy's decisions as they always led to something great.

All of this went through my head in a matter of seconds before I made my decision and stepped into my future.

I started by sharing with Jim what I had discovered in Savy's folder. I had brought the folder with me, and we poured over it together. Jim grew excited as he saw the possibilities of Savy's vision and plans for the inn, especially from the viewpoint of a future doctor.

He chuckled and said, "That's my grandpa."

"Jim, all I can say is that I'm all in on coming aboard. I love the idea and want to be a part of it, but I do have some family commitments that come first. My mom is seriously sick, and I have to be there for her."

Jim expressed his agreement and understanding. "As it should be, Sophie. Family always comes first."

With both of us excited and talking, Jim walked me over to the construction area to show me around. In only one week, they had made tremendous progress. Jim told me that there were two construction crews working on the expansion and that they were working almost around the clock.

"It's planned for the new section to be open two months from now," Jim said.

"That is amazing," I responded. I started feeling a bit of panic setting in. It was as if Jim sensed my energy and responded.

"Sophie, don't feel rushed. Take all the time you need to make the transition. I will work with your schedule to get you started slowly. School starts in three months, but if I need to postpone again, I will."

"But what if the school objects to another postponement? I don't want to cause a problem," I said anxiously.

Jim chuckled again. "My grandfather made an endowment to the medical school and is sponsoring my education. Believe me, Sophie, there won't be a problem."

I took in a deep breath, sighed, and felt more relaxed. It was simply the logistics that needed to be worked out. I would also need to find a wonderful nanny to help with Little Savy.

Have faith, Sophie, were words that I heard quietly in my mind. Savy's communications were coming to me more frequently, and they weren't only happening in dreams. I heard subtle yet clear messages. I had become far more aware of the signs, messages, and symbols as Savy communicated in a variety of ways.

Late that afternoon, my family all met up in the lobby. Mom told me that Dad had taken a nap, and she had gone for a walk in the gardens. I hadn't told my parents about the offer for me to take over the inn, nor had I told them about the expansion plans. I decided to share it with them at some point during the weekend when it felt appropriate.

Our dinner reservation was scheduled for 6 p.m. Mom and Dad were used to eating early, and Little Savy was usually in bed by 8 p.m. every evening. Mom told me that she booked a couple's massage for the following morning for her and Dad. She also told me she scheduled a facial, manicure, and pedicure for the two of us on Saturday afternoon.

"Hope you don't mind that I went ahead and booked that, Soph. I thought it would be a fun thing for the two of us to do, and the boys can hang out together."

"Works for me, Mom." I turned to Benny. "My love? What about you? Are you okay with this? It means you and Dad are on baby duty."

"No problem, honey. Dad, Little Savy, and I can go on a horse and buggy ride through the trails. They tour around the entire lake. I read about it on the pamphlet in the suite. They offer individual rides or group rides, and I can ask George to arrange something for us at the same time you and Mom go to the spa."

It was as if Benny forgot something and turned to me to say, "They also offer babysitting services, and since there is a singer performing tonight in the piano bar, perhaps we can enjoy a set or two after Little Savy is in bed."

"Wonderful idea!" I exclaimed. "Mom? Dad? Are you on board with that?"

"Sounds lovely," Mom replied.

Every part of the weekend was nothing short of divine. Mom and Dad were thrilled with their experience staying there, and once I shared the plan that I would run it one day, they loved the idea. They were impressed with the expansion plans too. Considering Mom was potentially someone who could appreciate the environment for end-of-life care, her opinion mattered. She agreed that the idea of Sophie's Magical Inn sounded both comforting and serene.

Over the weekend, Benny and I discussed the idea of moving, running the inn, and his career. Benny confessed to me that he really wanted to be a stay-at-home dad. I was stunned by that, as he had never mentioned that before. Besides, he had a phenomenal career and seemed to be totally into his job. He said he loved his career but loved being with Little Savy more. I could certainly appreciate that and felt so grateful for his decision.

Once we returned home, we decided we would put our house on the market, begin looking for a new home located near the inn, and Benny would hand in his resignation.

I resolved that the drive to Mom and Dad's house was only an hour and a half, and we would visit them often.

My dear Benny had been right. Everything was working out perfectly.

Chapter 16

The next two months went by quickly. According to Mom's doctor, the cancer had stopped growing. The doctor didn't define her situation as being in remission but did confirm it was rare for this to happen. As a family, we were all happy to see that she didn't appear to be getting worse and seemed to have more good days than bad ones lately.

When I went with Mom to the most recent appointment, her doctor pulled me aside and suggested we begin to plan for palliative care.

I was surprised that he was suggesting palliative care when she didn't look like she needed it. "But she seems better. Why would we do that? Maybe since the cancer isn't growing, she will live much longer than the six months you forecasted."

"I've seen this before, Sophie. Your mom is not going to get better. She may be fine right now or appear fine, but she is going to get worse, and I suspect it will happen very soon. Simply be aware and prepared," the doctor firmly suggested.

Within days of returning from our trip to the inn, Benny handed in his resignation, giving two weeks' notice. He had a well-trained assistant who could take over right away. He decided to stop working immediately so I could direct my attention to the inn before we moved.

Two times a week, I would drive to the inn for long meetings with Jim and other key staff. They kept me abreast of the status of the construction and consulted with me on decisions that needed to be made.

Additional staff, including medical professionals, were being hired to properly care for the upcoming patient-guests who would be checking into the special end-of-life section of the inn. We decided that instead of calling them simply guests, we would refer to them as patient-guests.

Jim and I scheduled the grand opening around his departure date and put together a full-scale media campaign.

Even though Jim's departure was rapidly approaching, he was still very actively involved in the day-to-day operations and promised he would only be a phone call away if I needed anything after he went to med school.

I learned so much from Jim in a short amount of time, and my confidence grew daily that I would be successful in my new role.

Benny and I began house-hunting immediately after the decision was made to move. We found a one-year-old, stunningly gorgeous, high-quality, custom-designed stately home within a five-minute drive from the inn. The house prices were much better in the country, and we were pleasantly surprised to find a home that we loved so quickly. We thought the buying and selling was going to be a time-consuming process, and it wasn't. We booked an appointment with a realtor and scheduled visits to see half a dozen houses. The second home we visited was the one we chose.

When we pulled into the driveway of the home, we both started to feel a connection. I heard Savy say, *This is the one, Sophie.* The property was magnificent. Even though the home was newly built, there were many trees on the two-acre property. Once we walked into the foyer, we were hooked. I took one look at Benny's face and knew we were in our new home. I turned to the realtor and suggested he begin to draw up the paperwork as our search was over. He chuckled and asked if we wanted to see the rest of the home. I told him, "When you know, you know."

Our new home had five bedrooms and six bathrooms. Each of the bedrooms had a bathroom attached. The master bedroom was enormous, and attached to the master was an adorable nursery. I had never seen anything like it in a home before. A nursery attached to the master bedroom was divine. Everything about this home was perfect for us.

The entire open-concept home was on one level and had extremely high ceilings. It was designed in a u-shape, and the backyard was set up like a courtyard with a pool, hot tub, sauna, stone waterfall, play area, cabana, firepit, and an outdoor kitchen.

The previous owners must have had a baby or toddler because everything was well designed with safety in mind for small children. The hot tub had a special cover on it that couldn't be opened easily by children. The backyard was fenced, but there was also a special safety fence around the pool that could be inserted or removed at will. The colors in the home were perfect for our taste too. It felt as if this home was made for us.

We absolutely loved the neighborhood. The houses were unique and custom designed. All the other homes on the street were on two-acre lots as well, and there was a park within walking distance. The community was built in a section of town where there were acres of crown land surrounding it. Our new home had no rear neighbors, and because we backed onto crown land, there would never be anyone behind us.

Our existing home was sold before the sign was placed on the lawn. When we called our realtor to let him know we would be selling our home, he said one of the realtors in his office was working with a potential out-of-town buyer looking to buy a luxury home in our neighborhood.

Our realtor came over with a professional photographer and videographer, and they captured a couple of hundred photos and a video walkthrough. He sent it to the realtor, who, in turn, sent it to the buyer, and they bought the home without visiting. The buyer agreed to our sale price, and the closing date would be one week later than our new home possession date.

It was wonderful to have the house sale and purchase organized so that I could focus on my family and my new career. Officially I would be taking over the inn when the grand opening occurred. In the meantime, with Jim's guidance, I was familiarizing myself with the day-to-day operations. At night I would study Savy's vision for the inn and make my own notes. I wanted to ensure that I was honoring his wishes and creating the fulfillment of his vision exactly as he desired.

My compensation to run the inn still hadn't been discussed. I was a little embarrassed and finally brought the subject up to Jim, and he just patted my arm and said, "Don't worry, we'll hear from the lawyers soon, Sophie, just trust me. Now let's go over those figures you were asking me about."

Our move was coming up, and I began to feel some trepidation. Were we doing the right thing with Benny quitting his job, me accepting this role, selling our home, and moving out to the country? These were all big life changes. Every time I began to have this feeling, I would hear Savy's voice say, *It is all unfolding perfectly as it should.*

One evening I had a frightening nightmare. I dreamed I was freefalling from the sky. I was hundreds of feet in the air and falling to the earth. I was terrified I would hit the ground. Thankfully I woke up before that happened. I wondered if the nightmare was indicative of the fear of failure. I immediately dismissed that thought.

It was the middle of the night, and I turned to look at my husband. Benny was sleeping soundly. I slipped out of bed and went into our family room. The moon was shining brightly, and it illuminated the room. Something caught my attention. I turned to look at the photo that I had on the mantle above the fireplace. It was a photo of me, Benny, and Savy on our wedding day. There were words illuminated and written across the photo: *I am with you always, in all ways*. I turned on the light, looked back at the photo, and the words had disappeared.

That had to be a sign from Savy. I knew, from that moment on, there was nothing to be terrified about. Everything was going to turn out exactly as it should.

The next day my dad called me. "Sophie, Mom has been taken by ambulance to the hospital. She is being evaluated right now, but they think she had a heart attack."

"What? Oh, my goodness. She was doing so well. Benny is home, so I can come right away. I will be there within thirty minutes."

I raced to the hospital feeling an abundance of anxiety. *Stay calm, Sophie, stay calm*, I heard. Savy was guiding me once again. With that assurance, I took some deep breaths.

When I arrived at Emergency, I found my dad right away. He knew I was coming and came down to greet me. Mom was already in a room in the intensive care department. Dad led me to see her. I walked into her hospital room, and even though she was hooked up to a heart monitor that was beeping away, she looked fine. I must have had a look of wonder on my face as she spoke first. "Sophie, I'm fine, I'm fine. It was a minor heart attack, and they are keeping me for a bit to monitor things."

"What happened?"

"I went into the washroom and suddenly broke out in a cold sweat. Nausea consumed me, and I started vomiting. Next, I began to feel light-headed, so I sat down on the floor. I was concerned I was going to pass out. Dad heard the commotion and walked in to check on me. When he saw the condition I was in, he called an ambulance right away."

Dad broke in. "Brandy and Clancy are on their way."

"I don't want you guys to make a fuss. I'm fine. I really am." Mom didn't want us to worry about her. She never wanted to be a burden on anyone. She could see the toll her situation was taking on Dad, and she felt bad about that.

The doctor decided to keep her overnight for observation. Dad asked for a cot to be brought into her room so that he could stay with her.

Perhaps this is what her cancer doctor was referring to. She had been doing so well. I genuinely hoped she was taking a turn for the better, but her situation wasn't promising. I wondered if she might consider coming to the inn when it was time for her to have more care. I knew Dad wouldn't be able to take care of her when things got worse, and according to the doctor, her health was destined to get a whole lot worse.

I decided to broach the subject of bringing Mom to the inn with Dad, Brandy, and Clancy at the earliest possible opportunity. She didn't have to go there in the next day or two, but we could consider it when the time was right.

Mom was going to be discharged the following day. Since Dad was staying at the hospital, I invited Clancy and Brandy over to our home for a family meeting to discuss the next steps for Mom. I told them about the end-of-life care that could be provided for Mom at the inn. They were both open to whatever was best for her. I appreciated their flexibility as it would mean extra driving for them unless they wanted to check into the inn.

That evening Jim called to ask about my mom and to tell me that he had something to give to me when I was able to come into the office. When I asked what it was, he said that he'd show me the next time we saw each other. I was curious as to what it was and wondered why he didn't just tell me on the phone.

On the heels of the thoughts of curiosity, I heard Savy whisper, *You're going to love this one, Sophie!*

Chapter 17

After Mom's minor heart attack, she was released from the hospital and returned home. Within days her health began declining rapidly. She was sleeping more and unable to get up easily and go to the washroom, nor was she strong enough to bathe herself. Dad was doing his best, but it was difficult for him to manage.

The doctor told Dad that it was time for hospice care. He had approved of the facility at the inn after having a telephone conversation with the new in-house physician who was brought on to take care of the patient-guests.

It was time for me and Benny to move, and thankfully we hired an excellent moving company to pack the entire house, move everything, and unpack at our new home. We were both extremely grateful to have this service as it allowed us to focus on Mom and easily get settled in our home. The movers put everything away so that our entire home was organized and ready for us to use.

The construction was finished at the inn, and the new facility was completely impressive. New staff had been hired, and a few patient-guests had already moved into suites with family members to prepare for their end-of-life transition.

As part of our media campaign, television and radio outlets received press releases about the expansion and the name change, and even though we hadn't had our official grand opening, the news was being shared widely. By the response from the community, it appeared there was a need for what we were offering at Sophie's Magical Inn.

Instead of putting Mom in the new section, we decided to have Mom and Dad stay in Savy's suite. This felt like the right thing to do. A hospital bed was brought into the main living room area of the suite. Dad would be able to sleep in the king-size bed in the suite's bedroom.

Jim arranged for Brandy and Steve to have the room next door, and Clancy and Allison were given the room across the hall from them. Benny and I would stay at our new home as it was only a five-minute drive away.

Jim was getting ready to leave for med school but was still managing activities at the inn. I wasn't spending as much time with him as I was focused on being with

Mom. Jim was very supportive of the situation, and we were very appreciative.

As a family, we decided to have a family member stay with Mom around the clock. This also gave Dad a chance to get some rest. Mom was never alone. An intravenous with a morphine drip to help with the pain was administered. She was sleeping most of the time and barely conscious.

One evening, as I was sitting beside her bed and Dad was asleep, I heard Savy whisper to me, *If there is anything you want to say to her, say it now*. This startled me as I thought she was about to pass on. As soon as I felt the emotion of anxiousness about her passing, Savy spoke again, *Not yet, Sophie, but soon*.

It was close to midnight, and I was awake as I sat beside Mom's bed. I was staring at her and thinking of the many ways she was a great mom. She had never once told me she loved me, but I knew she did. As I was watching her, she turned her head toward me and opened her eyes. She smiled ever so softly and began to speak. I could barely make out her words but heard the message clearly.

"Our baby girl Sophia, you are so loved. I've always loved you and always will. Dad and I are so proud of the woman you have become. I will watch over you, Benny, and Little Savy as I will watch over all my children and grandchildren. Know that I will be with you always."

Her words touched my heart. I began to cry.

"Create lasting memories that make your heart sing, Sophie. Embrace life as it is a gift. Know that I am going to a better place and will be reunited with Braden. I will see you in your dreams." And with that promise, she closed her eyes and drifted back to sleep.

Tears gently fell down my cheeks. "I love you too, Mom."

I stayed beside Mom's bed all night long, and even though I was seated upright, I did manage to drift in and out of sleep. In the morning, Brandy came into the suite with coffee for Dad and me. She offered me her room to have a nap as Steve had left for work. He had a meeting that he simply couldn't miss and planned to return later that afternoon. I decided to go home to see

Benny and Little Savy and take a shower and freshen up.

That day the doctor visited Mom, and after examining her, he called a family meeting. Benny, Little Savy, and I had returned just in time to meet with the doctor and the others. He informed us that Mom's transition was swiftly approaching. It was difficult for him to determine exactly how much time she had, but he said it could be a matter of hours or a day or two, but it certainly wouldn't be weeks.

There was silence in the room. The doctor broke the silence by saying, "You will know when the time is approaching as she'll start something called the death rattle. Her breathing will become labored, and she'll have a gurgling sound when she breathes. Do not be alarmed. Call the nurse, and she will help you through it."

As a family, we decided that anyone who wanted to be with Mom could be in the suite, and we wouldn't restrict anyone. Braden's children arrived with Clancy's children, and the four of them sat beside Mom's hospital bed, two on each side.

One by one, each family member said their goodbyes. It was beautiful, touching, and sad at the same time. Mom's breathing was becoming labored, and the death rattle commenced. Dad appeared to be already overcome with grief. He would cry silently, and we could see, by the look on his face, he was already in deep emotional pain.

It was dinnertime, and all the grandchildren went to the restaurant to get something to eat. Lilly offered to take Little Savy with them. Little Savy loved Lilly and enjoyed being surrounded by his cousins.

We knew Mom's passing was quickly approaching. The nurse joined us in the suite and offered to stay in case we needed her. She assured us that the passing would be tranquil.

Allison, Steve, and Benny joined the grandchildren in the restaurant. Dad and Clancy were on one side of mom's bed, and Brandy and I were on the other. Suddenly Mom turned her head forty-five degrees to the right and tilted her head upward. It appeared as if she was looking at something, but her eyes were closed. She raised her right arm and extended her hand as if she was going to take someone else's hand. I looked in that direction and saw a silhouette of Savy standing there with his hand extended to her.

"Oh my God!" I could see Savy's silhouette clearly. "Can you see him?" I asked the others.

"See who?" Brandy responded.

Mom gasped and took her last breath. She was gone.

Chapter 18

One can never be completely prepared for a loved one's passing, no matter whether you knew it was coming or not. When Mom took her last breath, I remember feeling an overwhelming sense of loss. Since Savy's spirit was there to greet her, I assumed they were together, but the reality of never seeing her again made me feel I had lost an anchor and was adrift.

Prepared or not, it was an incredibly sad moment. Dad broke down instantly. He was consumed in sadness. I had seen him cry before but not in this manner. He gently propped himself up onto Mom's bed and laid down beside her. He stroked her face and repeated, "My sweet angel, my sweet angel."

I looked toward Clancy, and he had tears flowing down his face too. He gestured toward Dad and shrugged his shoulders. He whispered to me that he was at a loss as far as how to console him or if we should console him. Brandy was quietly crying and looking down at her hands. It appeared as if Brandy was silently praying.

Suddenly Savy's silhouette appeared again. He was standing beside the bed. He had his hand extended toward the bed again as if he were offering his hand to my dad. "Savy, what are you doing?" I spoke out loud. I didn't understand what was going on. Both Clancy and Brandy looked at me, then looked in the direction where I was focusing, and then looked back at each other. They obviously couldn't see Savy.

Savy didn't answer me and stayed focused on my dad. Abruptly Dad grabbed his chest as if he was in pain. He took a deep breath, reached his hand out toward Savy, and then he lost consciousness.

The nurse had left the suite because Mom had already passed, and she wanted to give us some private time.

Brandy shouted to Clancy, "Go and get the nurse!" Clancy stood up and ran out of the room.

Savy's silhouette disappeared, and Dad was gone. I checked his pulse, and there wasn't one. Clancy returned with the nurse, and she began CPR while Brandy, Clancy, and I looked on.

I could not believe this was happening. I couldn't absorb the magnitude of this loss. Both my parents! This can't be. I was not prepared for this. None of us were.

The nurse tried to revive Dad for several minutes but to no avail. He was dead. She turned to us and said sadly, "I am so sorry, but he is gone."

I could hardly breathe. I started to pace the floor as I didn't know what to do. Savy began to speak to me. I could hear him clearly, but the others couldn't.

Sophie, I know you are consumed in grief at this moment but remember what I shared with you in your dream. Both your Mom and Dad are in a better place. Your dad didn't want to go on without your mom. He literally died from a broken heart. His heart failed him. The passing of your mom was too much for him. He may not have been the best husband in the early years of their marriage, but he loved her with all his heart. Take comfort in knowing that they are together in eternity.

As Savy was speaking to me, I began to repeat his words for Clancy and Brandy. I wasn't sure if they would believe that I was hearing Savy's words, but they were completely captivated as I spoke. Savy went on.

If you knew how free their souls are now, you would not be sad. They are free from pain. They are happy. They are at peace now. They are in the most beautiful place. Allow the memories of your mom and dad to serve as a source of joy. Remember to simply think of them, and they are with you in your thoughts and in your heart.

They ask that you dry those tears. They are eternally united. They loved you all very much and will guide you as your angels. They will be with you forever.

Savy's words brought comfort to us all. The nurse returned after reporting his death and suggested we leave the room and allow them to take care of the bodies. The spouses and grandchildren were still in the restaurant, and we decided to go and join them and tell them the news. We knew it wasn't going to be easy, but we also realized we had to be strong for them.

As a family, we made plans for the funeral. Mom and Dad had chosen a burial plot beside Braden and would be laid to rest there. As much as Savy had enlightened me on the grieving process, the loss of both parents was inconceivable. I knew it was going to take some time to heal from this pain, and I would rely on Savy's wisdom to help me through it.

When sadness came over me, I would switch my attention to a thought that would invite a better feeling, just as Savy taught me. I'd think of a memory of Mom and Dad: *Dad putting together a bicycle for Christmas with a big grin. Mom happily serving her famous pineapple cake.* I gave thanks over and over for the blessings they brought to our lives. The saddest part for me was the thought that Little Savy wouldn't get to know his grandma and grandpa, but he could get to know of them through our family sharing the memories, and that is what we would do.

I also felt confident that I could communicate with their spirits in a similar manner as I had with Savy's. Perhaps they would also send me messages in my dreams or in other creative ways.

Jim took it upon himself to create a memorial tree garden. He hired a landscape crew to design this area in the back garden behind the new end-of-life section of the inn. It was beautiful, and the first two trees planted were dedicated to Mom and Dad. Jim said a tree would be planted for every patient-guest who transitioned from the beautiful setting that was Savy's legacy, as trees were symbolic of the cyclical nature of life. My family and I were deeply touched by this thoughtful gesture.

After the funeral for my parents, I directed my attention back to running Sophie's Magical Inn. It was time for the grand opening and time for Jim to head off to medical school.

Just prior to the grand opening ceremony, Jim pulled me aside. He said, "Sophie, I meant to give this to you earlier, but with everything that transpired, it didn't feel like the timing was right." He extended his hand with an envelope.

After taking the envelope, I could see that my name was written on the outside and it was Savy's handwriting. "What is this?" I was puzzled, to say the least.

"Savy gave this to me a month before he passed on. As you know, his vision was for this inn to be run by you. He had big plans for you, but only if you were open to them and accepted them. He instructed me to give you this envelope only when you accepted the role. I am aware of the content, and I believe you're going to enjoy reading this." He had a big smile on his face.

"Do I open it now?" I asked.

"Yes. Definitely!"

I walked over to a corner of the room, sat down on one of the lobby sofas, and pulled the letter out of the envelope. It was from Savy.

My dear Sophie,

If you are reading this letter, then it means you have accepted the role of running a very special place. Thank you, I am grateful. You had a choice, and I believe you chose well.

I knew, in my heart, you were the perfect person to take on this responsibility. I trust you, and I believe you will bring to life my vision for a unique place for those who desire to evolve, grow, or transition.

This inn is a spot that I discovered many years ago. I came here on business. The first time I checked in, I knew it was extraordinary. I was told that the building was built on land that has extraordinary energies for healing. Every time I came here, I felt uplifted.

Every one of us comes to this earthly plane with a purpose. Some discover why they were born and live their life fulfilling their life's purpose, while others struggle. As you know, it doesn't have to be that way, and I know you will help others in only positive and beneficial ways. That is your purpose.

Thank you for taking the torch. Thank you for sacrificing yourself without any expectation of anything in return. You are an unconditionally giving person. I love that about you.

Now I have a gift for you. Are you ready?

I am gifting you with ownership of this inn. It is now yours, dear Sophie. This is my gift to you. Do with it what you wish. I had a vision for expansion, and now this vision has been shared with you, and this is now your inn.

Funds have already been set aside for the renovations and the addition. All expenses will be fully covered. The inn is profitable and brings in income, but it is up to you to keep it going and growing. This is your baby now, and I have faith you will give this your all, as you have done with every assignment, project, or goal that you have taken on.

Maintain that spirit of serving. Stay true to leaving everyone you meet with the impression of increase. There are no limits to what you can accomplish. Perhaps you may consider creating more of these inns around the world. I may not have included that in my expansion plans, but the sky is the limit.

Always remember to have fun in everything you do. Keep your values as your priority, and remember to keep the main thing the main thing.

Your loving friend,

P.S. I know what you are thinking right now, Sophie. Yes, this is yours. I instructed my lawyers to take care of the legal documents. You will receive the deed via courier when everything is ready. And don't be concerned about Jim, as he's all set. His grandfather set him up for life ;-) Jim is pursuing his vision of being a doctor and would probably love to come and work at the inn if you are open to it, but I'll leave that decision with the new owner—you.

I looked up and saw Jim watching me from afar. He was smiling. I nodded my head, and he nodded back. I searched the room for Benny and Little Savy, who had joined us for the grand opening ceremony. I saw them walking toward me, smiles on both of their faces. I couldn't wait to share this news with my husband. I knew that life was just about to get a whole lot better. I heard Savy's voice as I began to get up from the sofa:

Today is a brand-new day, Sophie. It is the beginning of something truly magical at Sophie's Magical Inn.

And with that, the celebration began.

The End

Did You Love This Book, And Do You Desire More Savy Wisdom?

Everything that Savy taught Sophie can be accessed instantly in Peggy McColl's incredible online program, *Savy's Proven Success Principles.*

- If you'd love to heal...
- If you'd love to get unstuck...
- If you'd love to create prosperity...
- If you'd love to positively impact people...
- If you'd love to make the rest of your life, the best of your life...

Explore what's next for you now!

Learn More:
{ www.SavyWisdom.com/SPSP }

Proven Success Principles

Implement The Power of Savy Wisdom™ in Your Life with Savy's Proven Success Principles

"You see, the secret to life is to feel joy and freedom while continuously holding the intention of what you want. Even though it may not be in your life at the moment and there may not be any evidence of it in sight, stay connected to what you would love as if it is already here. That's how you draw what you want to you. By doing this, you activate the life-affirming power within you."
  – Savy

How Would You Love To:
- Upgrade your self-expression
- Upgrade your home
- Upgrade your income
- Upgrade your relationships
- Upgrade your joy
- Upgrade your business

Get Started:
{ **www.SavyWisdom.com/SPSP** }

Savy's Proven Success Principles Contains Simple, Easy To Follow Video Lessons And Life-Changing Tools...

Expand Your Awareness

What are you choosing to focus on? It's time to expand your awareness to the tremendous power deep within you. Create your own GIMY journal to effectively build paradigms that will serve you in only positive ways.

Discover Your Passion

What would you love? We were all given a gift at birth; the gift of choice. Create the ideal life - no more "tip toe-ing" through life hoping you will make it safely to death. Remember, you don't need to know the HOW.

Achieve Your Goals and Dreams

What do you need to believe in order to accomplish your goals and dreams? Through effective use of your imagination and creation of your own SABY journal, all you desire is already yours.

Live From The End

Get clarity around your passion and learn to look for the good in every situation. Through spaced time repetition you will learn to live from the end. Discover the power of living in state of gratitude all day long. This new found belief will be your key to success.

Move Into Action

There are many roads to get to your destination – learn how to choose the "right" road or the most direct way. Discover what actions will move you in the right direction.

Stay In Alignment

With magic when you know how it works, the magic disappears. With life when you know how it works, the magic begins. Learn how to stay away from the negative and how to instantly switch into the positive.

About The Author

Peggy McColl has dedicated her life to making a positive difference in the lives of hundreds of millions of people around the world, from her immediate family to cherished readers like you. She is a world-renowned wealth, business and manifestation expert as well as the New York Times Best Selling Author of *Your Destiny Switch: Master Your Key Emotions And Attract the Life of Your Dreams.*

Throughout her career, Peggy has been coined "Your Destiny Maker" and "The Prosperity Mentor". She has worked with – and been endorsed by – other icons in the personal development field, from Bob Proctor and Neale Donald Walsch to Mark Victor Hansen and Marianne Williamson.

Peggy's books, events and online programs inspire and instruct people to heal their past, reach their maximum potential, take massive quantum leaps and truly create their own destiny by design through simple, step-by-step self-realization.

To explore more ways Peggy can help you reach your goals and live your dreams, please visit:

{   **<u>www.PeggyMcColl.com</u>**   }